HYDROFOIL SAILING

Icarus, *flying faster than the wind* (*photo* Yachting World)

Hydrofoil Sailing

ALAN J. ALEXANDER, BSc, MSc, PhD, CEng, AFRAeS, MIMechE

JAMES L. GROGONO, MB, FRCS

DONALD J. NIGG, BSEE, MBA

with a Foreword by
H.R.H. THE DUKE OF EDINBURGH KG, PC, KT, GBE, FRS

JUANITA KALERGHI 51 WELBECK STREET LONDON W1M 7HE

Published in Great Britain in 1972 by Juanita Kalerghi
© 1972 A. J. Alexander, J. L. Grogono, D. J. Nigg
All rights reserved. No part of this publication
may be reproduced in any form or by any means
without the prior permission of Juanita Kalerghi
ISBN 0 903238 00 4

Designed and printed at
The Curwen Press, Plaistow, London E.13

Contents

List of Illustrations

Foreword by H.R.H. THE DUKE OF EDINBURGH

I was tempted to try the idea of fitting hydrofoils to a sail-driven boat in 1956. *Fairey Fox* was designed by Uffa Fox and came out as a 24-foot gunter-rigged planing dinghy. (He refers to her in his book *Sailing Boats*.) The hydrofoils were to be supplied by Fairey Marine—hence the name of the boat. However I regret to say that nothing came of the project, although exactly what went wrong escapes me. I kept the boat and had some very exhilarating sailing with her as she could do 16 knots with the helmsman's heart only half way into his mouth. Judging by her conventional performance and handling I shudder to think what she might have done with foils.

The art has obviously advanced a good deal since those days and it is obvious from this book that a lot of homework has been done on the theory, mathematics and engineering problems involved. It now looks as if there is a real chance that sailing hydrofoils will begin to appear in numbers on the yachting scene.

Like all new developments there is a lot to be learnt and I daresay that anyone starting out on sailing hydrofoils will go through some very interesting and unusual experiences before all the snags are ironed out. However, judging by the results obtained by the authors of this book the effort and the occasional surprises are well worth it.

Buckingham Palace
1972

Introduction

FOIL-SAILING is amongst the newest of water sports, and is certainly one of the most exhilarating. Although it is over thirty years since the first successful 'flight' of a man-carrying craft, under sail power alone, the lack of a commercial outlet has made development rather slow. However, in recent years advances in conventional yacht design and construction have aided the experimental foil-sailor in many ways, and new designs appear frequently. Foil-sailing is now within the grasp of any small-boat sailor who becomes interested.

This book, like foil-sailing itself, is a compromise. In foil-sailing the compromise is between theoretical perfection and practical attainability; in the book the compromise is between the 'text-book' approach, providing an accurate—but perhaps boring—account of the relevant theory, and the 'entertainment' approach, consisting of an illustrated and anecdotal account of foil boats and foil-sailors. It is hoped that neither of these aspects has suffered at the hands of the other, although some sections will doubtless be of more interest to one person than another. The early chapters are devoted to theory, moving on gradually to more applied aspects; any interested person should find the theory within his grasp, and take the book as a whole. The less mathematical must not be dismayed by the free use of mathematical symbols in the early chapters; the symbols are used in simple equations to clarify the expression of various relationships, and little mathematical knowledge is required. All symbols are defined when first introduced, and there is a full key on page 95. The more mathematical may wish to seek the derivations from the literature, to which reference is made in the bibliography. The would-be foil-sailor will find ample factual material, with working examples, to enable him to design his foils aright.

The first three chapters review the aspects of fluid dynamics related to foil-sailing, and the next three are concerned with the problems of stability and foil design. The last three chapters describe the successful craft, mainly in the accounts of their originators. These accounts are all of man-carrying craft which have flown under sail power alone. Models have been excluded because of the dangers and pitfalls in scaling; the use of foils for stabilization only has been excluded because it is a separate subject in itself. For an account giving more emphasis both to models and foil-stabilization, reference should be made to the Amateur Yacht Research Society (AYRS) publication No. 74, *Sailing Hydrofoils*.

The authors wish to express their gratitude to all the foil-sailors for their contributions, to Mr John Gillett for his graphics, and to Juanita Kalerghi, without whom this book would not have come into being.

ALAN J. ALEXANDER

JAMES L. GROGONO

DONALD J. NIGG

CHAPTER 1

Why Hydrofoils?

THE READER may well ask 'why sail on hydrofoils?' What is wrong with a good strong hull and keel? Why replace them with fragile and awkward appendages which affect the draught and pick up debris? The answer lies in the greater potential speed that the foils provide. The use of boats, of a sort, to transport people and goods goes back to the dawn of history. On occasions, perhaps, it did not matter how long it took to cross a river, and a tree trunk or simple raft made from branches was adequate. The exigencies of war, athletic competition, and more recently, commerce, have led to improvements in design, the usual requirement being more speed, with comfort and safety often given little consideration.

How does one increase speed on any vehicle, be it moped or Jumbo-Jet, hovercraft or ocean liner? Unfortunately, it is a fact of life that if anything moves, or is caused to move, nature will provide a force to oppose that movement; on land this force is solid friction, in fluids it is viscous drag and wave drag. Most types of drag increase with speed, at least initially, and increases of speed therefore mean an increased expenditure of energy. Even if economic considerations are unimportant, merely increasing the size of power unit will not necessarily increase the speed. The power unit itself may become too large or too heavy for the size of craft envisaged, or the increased fuel consumption may restrict the range too much. It may be better to *reduce* the size of power unit and craft since it is the difference between the power available and power needed that is important and not the absolute magnitude of either. Special difficulties arise when the power available is limited, for example in manpowered aircraft and yachts of a specified class. In these cases one cannot increase available power so one must decrease drag to achieve higher speeds.

One measure of efficiency of many types of transport is their lift/drag ratio. The lift may be thought of as a positive, useful, load-carrying quantity, e.g. related to the number of passengers an aircraft can carry or the weight of cargo in a ship, and the drag is the villain whose price must be paid in order to move that load. The

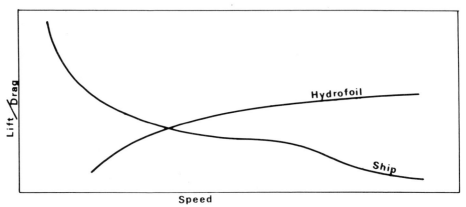

Fig. 1 Lift/drag against speed

ratio of lift or weight to drag of a ship is very high if the speed is low, but efficiency in this sense is useless if the craft is extremely slow; in general it must be fast to be competitive. Since the weight of a ship is constant (approximately, for a given journey) and its drag increases with speed, its efficiency will decrease with speed. The three main drag components of a ship are viscous or skin friction drag, wave drag and eddy-making resistance. At low speeds the viscous drag is the largest component, but at higher speeds the other components become important.

The weight of a ship is supported by hydrostatic pressure on the hull with very little lift coming from the ship's motion, whereas an aircraft derives its lift from the movement of air around its wings. The lift/drag ratio of a ship falls with increase in speed whereas the lift/drag ratio of an aircraft wing or hydrofoil increases from its minimum value at the stall to an approximately constant value at higher speeds (fig. 1). Hence at some speed the lifting wing principle will become more efficient than the floating hull and at that point it becomes more efficient for the ship to fly and not float. Moreover, as the speed increases still further the flying machine increases its superiority over its water-borne rival.

In order to see how lift is created dynamically by the movement of a foil through a fluid we turn to aerofoil theory since the mechanism of lift generation does not depend on the particular fluid and the principles are the same in air as in water, except when cavitation occurs (see Chapter 3). We shall consider, initially, only a particular section of the foil which is well away from the root and tip, and leave consideration of the effects of the proximity of these until later. In other words we are considering a two-dimensional flow where fluid is only allowed to move within and not through the plane of the paper.

A foil is usually of the general shape shown in fig. 2. This shows the flow pattern round the inclined section in an ideal fluid where viscosity is assumed to be negligible. The two points marked S_1 and S_2 are stagnation points where the fluid is brought to rest relative to the foil and the streamline AS_1S_2B marks the dividing line between the fluid which flows above the foil and that which flows beneath. Foils

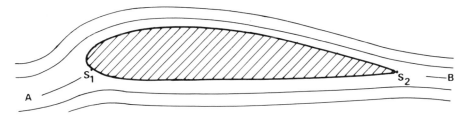

Fig. 2 Flow pattern of 'ideal' fluid around foil

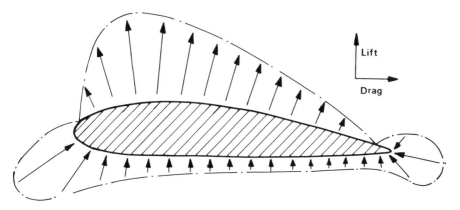

Fig. 3 Typical pressure distribution of a lifting foil

usually have a sharp trailing edge and the flow leaves the trailing edge smoothly. An increase in speed of a fluid changes its pressure and this relationship is expressed by Bernoulli's equation:

$$p_0 = p + \tfrac{1}{2}\rho u^2 + \rho gz \qquad [1]$$

where p_0 is the maximum pressure exerted at a stagnation point such as S_1 where the fluid is brought to rest, and p is the pressure at any other point in the fluid where the fluid velocity is u; ρ is the fluid density; z is the height above some datum level and g is acceleration due to gravity, $32 \cdot 2$ ft/sec^2. Thus as speed is increased the pressure drops. It is clear from fig. 2 that on average particles of fluid which move over the upper surface have further to travel than those which move over the bottom surface. They must travel faster in order to avoid creating a void in the fluid, and hence the general pressure will be lower on the upper surface than the lower surface. The small changes in height do not appreciably affect this argument. This creates a lift force and a typical pressure distribution of a lifting foil is shown in fig. 3. The arrows indicate the direction of the pressure forces (pressure measured relative to the fluid pressure well away from the foil) and it will be seen that in general the forces combine in the vertical (lift) direction and oppose each other in the horizontal (drag) direction thus giving high lift and low drag.

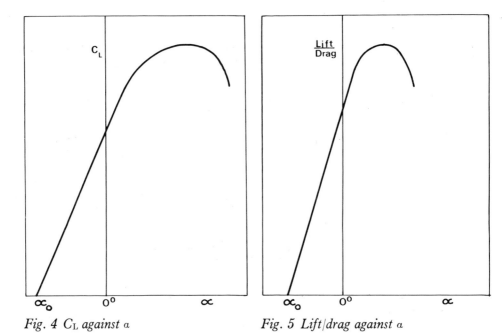

Fig. 4 C_L against α   *Fig. 5 Lift/drag against α*

The lift on a foil can be calculated from the formula:

$$\text{Lift} = \tfrac{1}{2}\rho\ U^2 S\ C_L \qquad\qquad [2]$$

where ρ is the density of the fluid
      U   is the speed of the foil
      S   is its plan area
      C_L is the lift coefficient.

The first three quantities are known in a given case and C_L may be obtained from books containing information on aerofoil sections, for example *Theory of Wing Sections*, Dover Publications Limited. The information is usually plotted as shown in fig. 4 where α is the inclination of the centre line of the foil to the fluid flow, and α_0 is the angle at which the lift is zero. It is seen that C_L increases with α up to a certain point, where the foil begins to stall, i.e. lift will start to decrease instead of increase with increasing α and 'buffeting' will occur. Reasons for the stall will be dealt with in the next chapter but it is sufficient to remark here that it should be avoided if possible.

Similarly the drag is calculated from the formula:

$$\text{Drag} = \tfrac{1}{2}\rho\ U^2 S\ C_D \qquad\qquad [3]$$

where C_D is the drag coefficient and may be obtained from graphs of the form shown in fig. 6.

For sailing craft the lift/drag ratio is more important than either lift or drag alone, and fig. 5 shows a typical curve, with the highest ratio at a low angle of attack usually between 0° and 3°.

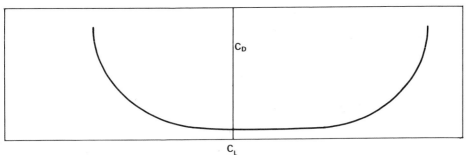

Fig. 6 C_D against C_L

A simple example will now be worked out to illustrate the use of the lift and drag formulae. It must be emphasized that there is no correction for 'end-losses' or surface proximity losses (Chapters 2 and 3).

Example

All-up weight of boat	= 500 lb.
Required take-off speed	= 10 knots

In order to apply the formulae the units used must be appropriate, i.e. with the weight of the boat in pounds, the density of water ρ is $1 \cdot 94$ slugs/ft³ (1 slug $= 32 \cdot 2$ lb. mass) and the velocity U in ft/sec. For ease of calculation, however, we may convert the formulae by a simple factor:

$$\text{Lift} = 2 \cdot 77 \ U^2 S C_L$$
$$\text{Drag} = 2 \cdot 77 \ U^2 S C_D$$

Lift and drag in pounds, U in knots, S is foil area in square feet. For take-off, substituting into the lift formula we have:

$$500 = 2 \cdot 77 \times 10^2 \times S \times C_L$$

Suppose from foil data we have chosen a section which gives a C_L value of $0 \cdot 5$ at an angle of incidence of $2°$ (where it may well have its highest lift/drag ratio). Then the required area:

$$S = \frac{500}{2 \cdot 77 \times 100 \times 0 \cdot 5}$$
$$= 3 \cdot 6 \text{ square feet}$$

With a drag coefficient C_D of $0 \cdot 007$, the total drag may be calculated as follows:

$$\text{Drag} = 2 \cdot 77 \times 10^2 \times 3 \cdot 6 \times \cdot 007$$
$$= 7 \cdot 00 \text{ lb.}$$

Both the area required, and the drag, will be greatly increased, however, by a variety of factors including dihedral angle, foil imperfections and end losses, as described in the next two chapters.

CHAPTER 2

Fully Submerged Hydrofoils

IN CHAPTER 1 we dealt with the elementary principles of lift generation in a two-dimensional ideal fluid flow. In real life we have to deal with a multitude of practical snags which, although they do not result in any changes in basic principles, nevertheless modify conditions to a greater or lesser degree.

The bête noire of fluid flow is the region close to a solid body such as a hull or a foil. This region is known as the 'boundary layer' and is responsible for almost all of the troubles which are encountered. In particular it is responsible for much of the drag, and also for stalling.

In order to appreciate how boundary layers influence the flow, let us first consider the changes in pressure and velocity which occur in an ideal flow around a streamlined body, fig. 7. If the fluid starts off with velocity U and pressure P it is brought to rest at the nose of the body and we have zero velocity and maximum pressure (Equation [1]). Further along the body the fluid accelerates reaching a higher velocity than U and a pressure less than P. The fluid then slows up near the trailing edge and pressure and velocity changes are the opposite of those which occurred upstream. In this case the fluid is changing its total store of energy represented by p_0 between kinetic energy $\frac{1}{2}\rho u^2$ and potential energy p. (For the sake of clarity we ignore changes in height so that the term 'ρgz' in Bernoulli's equation is negligible and $p_0 = p + \frac{1}{2}\rho u^2$.)

For an 'ideal' fluid, velocities near the solid surface can be quite high, but in a real fluid the forces of adhesion ensure that fluid molecules actually in contact with the surface always remain at rest relative to it. Thus the fluid velocities in the vicinity of the surface are very different in the ideal and the real fluid flow. For a fairly slender streamline body the fluid velocity in ideal flow would not vary very much in a direction y normal to the surface (it would, in fact, decrease slightly), whereas the velocity in a real flow would increase rapidly from zero on the surface to a maximum equal to the ideal fluid velocity U in a fairly small distance δ which is the boundary layer thickness, fig. 8. Thus in a real flow there are velocity gradients $\dfrac{du}{dy}$ (u varying with y) and it is known that stresses are generated in the

fluid equal to $\mu \times \dfrac{du}{dy}$, where μ is the fluid viscosity, and the total force on the body is

$\displaystyle\int \mu \left(\dfrac{du}{dy}\right)_{\text{surface}}$ where $\left(\dfrac{du}{dy}\right)_{\text{surface}}$ is the slope of the velocity curve (fig. 8) at

u = o and the symbol $\int$ means an integration or summation of these point stresses over the whole wetted surface.

Physically one may think of the viscous drag in terms of the force needed to deform the liquid (the velocity curve is an indication of this deformation) and although this is most easily visualized with movement in a very viscous liquid (say, treacle) it is true of all fluids, including gases. Thus a real fluid exerts a viscous drag on a body and if the body is large (e.g. a large ship) many thousands of horse-power will be required to overcome this drag at high speeds.

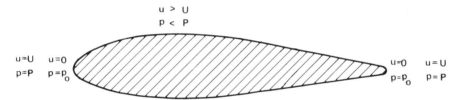

Fig. 7 Velocity changes in ideal flow

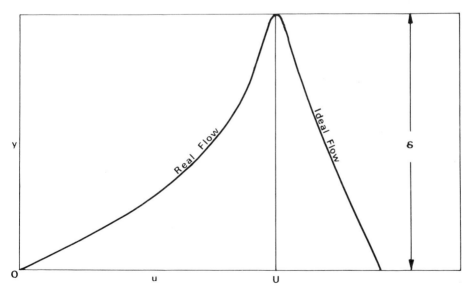

Fig. 8 Velocity gradients of real and ideal flow in boundary layer

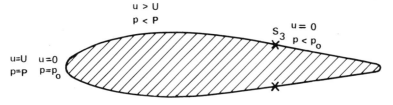

Fig. 9 *Velocity changes in real flow*

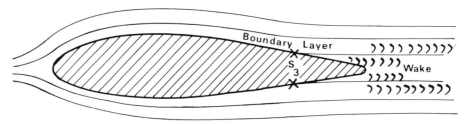

Fig. 10 *Boundary layer separation and wake*

There is, however, a secondary effect of a boundary layer on a fluid flow. We saw earlier (page 14) that with an ideal fluid an easy interchange was possible between pressure and velocity with the total pressure p_0 remaining constant. Unfortunately, due to the viscous stresses and consequent energy losses in the boundary layer, p_0 decreases with distance along the surface from the nose and the net result is that instead of the fluid reaching the trailing edge it has not sufficient energy and is brought to rest at some point S_3 ahead of the trailing edge, fig. 9. Beyond this point the flow is unable to proceed along the surface and separates from it, fig. 10, leaving a region of flow known as the 'wake' in which both velocities and pressure are low. This is exactly the same as the 'wake' behind a ship. The lower pressure at the rear of the body results in a pressure differential in the axial direction giving a pressure drag force. This is sometimes called 'form drag' since its magnitude depends on the form or shape of the body. For a streamline shape the skin friction drag is by far the largest drag component with only a small form drag but for 'bluff' bodies, e.g. cylindrical struts, the pressure drag is many times the skin friction drag.

Thus the boundary layer is responsible for all of the sectional (two-dimensional) drag and is also responsible for a small (10 per cent) reduction in lift from the ideal flow condition. Even so a well-designed foil will have a sectional lift/drag ratio of more than 100 for a lift coefficient of around 0·5, which is well below the stall.

Increasing the incidence of a foil will ultimately result in the foil stalling. This phenomenon is again due to the presence of boundary layers and the movement of the separation point S_3. As the incidence (and lift) is increased the velocities increase on the upper surface (Chapter 1) and hence the boundary layer losses increase. These increased losses mean that the separation point S_3 moves forward on the upper surface and at some point the lift will be affected and will ultimately decrease (the stall). With relatively thick sections ($\sim$15 per cent thickness/chord) the movement of this separation point is relatively steady and results in a well-rounded lift curve and a gentle stall, fig. 4. With very thin sections ($\sim$5 per cent thickness/chord) however, the movement forward of the separation point is very rapid and results in a very sudden and catastrophic stall, fig. 11. Although it is always the aim to avoid the stall and work on the straight part of the lift-curve slope, circumstances will almost inevitably arise when stalling will occur and careful thought should be given as to whether the advantages of thin sections (e.g. higher cavitation threshold speed, Chapter 3) outweigh this disadvantage in a particular situation. It should be emphasized that the above definitions of 'thick' and 'thin' aerofoils are somewhat arbitrary since thickness/chord ratio is only one factor which influences the stall. Another important factor is nose radius which does not necessarily depend on thickness/chord ratio. The severity of the stall, however, will become apparent when the experimental lift-incidence graph is obtained.

Up to this point we have considered only the sectional characteristics of foils but in practice, of course, every foil has to have ends, one of which will usually be a free end or tip. When the foil is lifting, the mean pressure on the lower surface is greater than that on the upper surface, and since there is no restriction to flow at the tip the high-pressure fluid tends to flow from bottom to top surface, fig. 12. Since the fluid is also moving past the wing in an axial direction, it tends to follow a 'corkscrew' path and forms what is known as a tip vortex, fig. 12. Also, at the extreme tip there is no pressure difference between top and bottom surfaces and hence no lift. The spanwise lift distribution is thus changed from approximately the sectional lift at the centre to zero at the tip. The curve is roughly elliptic and

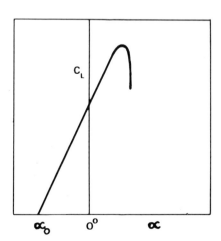

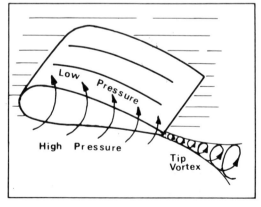

Fig. 11 C_L against α for thin section   Fig. 12 Loss of lift by tip effect and tip vortex

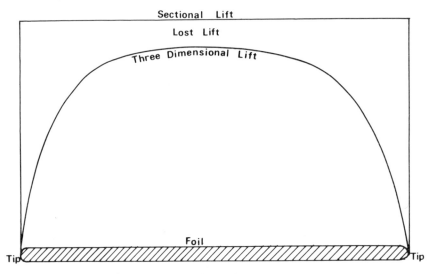

Fig. 13 Loss of lift for three-dimensional foil

this represents a considerable loss of lift on a three-dimensional wing with a tip compared with sectional values, fig. 13. Since the main loss of lift is near the tips, wings of large span (compared with the chord) lose less lift, relatively, than the wings of small span where flows at the tip may affect a large proportion of the span. The ratio span/chord is known as the 'aspect ratio' A and the lift change due to the effect of the tip is given by the formula:

$$\frac{C_{L3}}{C_{L2}} = \frac{A}{2+A} \qquad [4]$$

where C_{L3} is the lift coefficient of a foil with a tip and C_{L2} is the sectional lift coefficient. Strictly speaking this formula applies in ideal flow for a wing where the spanwise loading is of elliptic form, but is a good approximation for most practical cases.

These changes in lift distribution, and the changes in flow pattern due to tip vortices also result in an increase in drag. A new type of drag known as 'induced drag' and dependent on aspect ratio is created and is given by the formula:

$$C_{Di} = \frac{k\, C_{L3}^{2}}{\pi\, A} \qquad [5]$$

where k depends on the wing planform. For elliptical loading the value of k is $1 \cdot 0$ but in practice a figure of $1 \cdot 05$ is likely to give a reasonable answer.

It should be noted that the combined effects of lift reduction and increased drag due to the tip effect can seriously affect the value of lift/drag ratio. A good low drag shape having a sectional lift/drag ratio of $100+$ will be reduced to 30–40 when forming the section of a wing with an aspect ratio of 6. This is still relatively high, however, when it is remembered that some flat-bottomed, circular-arc-top sections have *sectional* lift/drag ratios which do not exceed 40.

Some hydrofoil boats use very low aspect ratio rectangular or delta wings to provide lift. These may be stronger, less likely to collect debris, and make the craft more manoeuvrable in narrow waters, but their efficiency is low. At very low aspect ratios around one the formulae given above do not strictly apply, although they indicate quite clearly that lift will be low and drag high. The effect of tip vortices on these narrow wings clearly dominates the flow and all wing edges are usually sharpened in order to facilitate the production of vortices at all incidences and thus avoid changes in flow regime which occur when the leading edges are rounded.

The lift for sharp-edged delta wings may be calculated from the formula:

$$C_L = 1 \cdot 23 \ A^{0 \cdot 77} a + 1 \cdot 59 \ A^{0 \cdot 6} a^{1 \cdot 74} \qquad [6]$$

This equation was derived from an analysis of experimental results obtained on sharp-edged delta wings. A similar formula is not available for low aspect ratio rectangular wings but the above formula could be used as a reasonable approximation. The drag is given by:

$$C_D = C_L \tan a \qquad [7]$$

When using results obtained from books and technical papers for design purposes, they will not normally have been obtained under the conditions in which it is proposed to use them and a problem of scaling arises. The relative speeds and sizes may be different as well as the properties of the fluid such as density ρ and viscosity μ since a good deal of testing is done in air. Scaling due to all of these factors is taken into account by considering the 'Reynolds number': R_e

$$R_e = \frac{\rho l U}{\mu} \qquad [8]$$

where U is the fluid or craft speed and l is a typical length (e.g. chord in the case of a foil). If l is in ft and U in ft/sec. the value of $\frac{\rho}{\mu}$ for water at 15°C is $7 \cdot 7 \times 10^4$ and for air $6 \cdot 3 \times 10^3$. Many of the standard results for aerofoil sections are available at a Reynolds number of 3×10^6. This is quite a convenient figure when it is realized that a one-foot chord foil moving at 20 knots (34 ft/sec.) has a Reynolds number of $2 \cdot 6 \times 10^6$. At Reynolds numbers less than about 10^6 appreciable changes may occur in C_L and C_D for a given incidence a but provided the Reynolds number exceeds 10^6 changes are usually small, and may be neglected if information at the correct Reynolds number is not available. Every effort should be made, however, to obtain information that is as near correct as possible.

Another factor that arises is the roughness and accuracy of the surface. Clearly the shape of the foil must be very close to its nominal shape since small variations in profile can give rise to large changes in C_L and C_D particularly if the foil is designed to have a low minimum value of C_D.

Only a very small amount of information is available on the change in performance due to the foil having an incorrect shape since most of the research has been done for aircraft work where the resources are available to ensure a correct profile. The amateur, with limited time and resources, must resign himself to producing an imperfect section and accept some penalty. Even with a basically correct section a slight waviness at the nose is found to reduce maximum lift/drag ratio by a factor of more than two. Similarly, a rough surface can affect the foil performance adversely, in an extreme case a reduction in lift/drag ratio by a factor of three has been recorded. Where roughness and waviness have been deliberately introduced on different parts of the foil surface for test purposes, it has been shown that the effects of profile distortions at the nose are by far the most important. Similar changes near the trailing edge have little effect. The moral to the amateur builder is clear; whatever time and effort are available should be lavished on the forward part of the section and particularly on the nose. This will ensure that the maximum performance is obtained for the minimum of effort.

CHAPTER 3

Surface-piercing Hydrofoils

UNTIL NOW we have considered the effects of a fluid of infinite extent moving past a body. This is true in the case of aircraft and of deeply submerged submarines, but for craft moving at the air-water interface an additional source of drag arises. As any small-boat sailor knows this problem is wave-making. Only two basic solutions are possible: (1) If sufficient power and therefore speed is available it is possible to outrun the wave system and hence avoid wave drag. This solution is in fact almost achieved by high speed planing craft and by hovercraft, but is virtually impossible in craft which are firmly 'water bound'. (2) Remove the hull from the water by replacing static lift (water displacement) by dynamic lift ('flying'), which is the hydrofoil solution. It should be noted that hovercraft are not in this category since the supporting cushion displaces water just as the hovercraft would do if it were floating. The hovercraft is virtually a displacement craft at low speed and suffers from wave drag; it gains its advantage from the fact that it is moving through air and not water and hence its skin friction drag is very low. There is thus more power available to outrun the wave system.

Any craft moving through water near to or on the surface will create waves and if the wavelength of these waves is such as to cause the bow of the craft to rise relative to the stern, the craft will experience wave drag due to the fact that a component of the thrust of the water on the hull acts in a rearward direction (fig. 14).

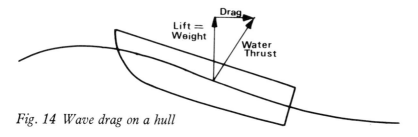

Fig. 14 Wave drag on a hull

Just as the Reynolds number is the scaling parameter for low speed flow in an infinite extent of fluid, so for free surface problems we have a parameter known as the 'Froude number' (F_n).

$$F_n = \frac{U}{\sqrt{lg}} \qquad [9]$$

where U is the craft or water speed and l is the length in feet.

The wave drag increases as the Froude number increases, reaching a maximum when the Froude number is in the range 0·6 to 1·0 (the value increases with the hull fineness ratio). A convenient formula for working out the 'hump speed' (speed at which maximum wave drag occurs) is, for a minimum Froude number of 0·6:

$$U_{HUMP} = 2·0 \sqrt{l} \text{ Knots} \qquad [10]$$

Clearly a hydrofoil boat must lift out of the water well before this speed is reached.

Hydrofoils are basically of two types, surface-piercing, and fully submerged. Surface-piercing foils are usually favoured for sailing boats because they are inherently stable. In general each foil will be carrying a fixed load, but if a transient extra load causes it to 'dig in', the lift will be increased thus causing it to rise back to its equilibrium position; clearly the reverse occurs if a foil lifts out. Thus a craft with two sets of foils, front and rear, will be stable in pitch, and for lateral stability the foils must be well separated in the transverse axis, and inclined at steep dihedral angles (Chapters 4 and 5).

Such an advantage as 'free' stability is not to be dismissed lightly, but surface-piercing foils have associated disadvantages. With a lifting foil the low pressures on the upper surface may tend to draw air down on to the foils, 'ventilation', and thereby cause a sharp loss of lift equivalent to a stall. In general this may be prevented by fixing 'fences' to the foils (see Chapter 6) and reduced by avoiding foil sections with 'peaky' pressure distribution.

A second disadvantage of some surface-piercing foils is that they effectively have two ends, a tip and the point at which the foil pierces the surface. Compared to the lift in water the lift of the part of the foil in air is negligible, owing to the difference in density, so there will be a fall off in lift near the surface. The lift may be calculated as for a three-dimensional wing:

$$\frac{C_{L3}}{C_{L2}} = 0·9 \frac{A}{2+A} \qquad [11]$$

where the factor 0·9 is necessary to bring the theoretical results in line with experimentally measured values, and the aspect ratio A is the submerged length divided by the chord, for a rectangular foil. If the foil is not rectangular, A is the (submerged length)² divided by the submerged area. The corresponding equation for induced drag, including an approximate experimental constant is:

$$C_{Di} = \frac{2·0\, C_{L3}^2}{\pi A} \qquad [12]$$

$$\text{Total drag } C_{D3} = C_{D2} + \frac{2 \cdot 0 \, C_{L3}^2}{\pi A} \qquad [13]$$

where C_{D2} is the section drag coefficient.

When using the lift formula the area used is the horizontal projected area and is equal to $S \times$ cosine θ, where θ is the dihedral angle and S the planform area.

Even with the yacht foil-borne and the hull well out of the water the effect of waves will still be felt. As a wave passes along the water surface water particles move in circular patterns about horizontal axes at right angles to the direction of motion; thus near the crest of the wave they are moving upwards and near the trough, downwards. As the hydrofoil moves towards the crest of the wave the upward motion of the water particles increases the incidence of the foil and thus the lift. So a hydrofoil will tend to ride the crest of the wave easily, but beyond the crest the motion of the water particles is downward, decreasing the foil incidence and lift. Thus the hydrofoil will tend to plough into the trough. All water particles perform this circular motion, although the motion reduces with depth, and thus the whole of the foil is affected and not just that part close to the surface.

The fact that the hydrofoil is designed to increase speed brings with it a potential problem. This is the problem of 'cavitation'. Cavitation is literally the boiling of water at atmospheric temperature but very low pressure. The vapour pressure of water at atmospheric temperature is about 35 lb./ft². As the speed of the water increases the pressure drops (Bernoulli, page 14), and eventually the pressure must reach vapour pressure. On a lifting foil the highest velocities and lowest pressures occur near the nose, see Chapter 1, and it is here that cavitation first occurs.

Just as with the Reynolds number and Froude number we have a parameter σ known as the 'cavitation number' and defined as:

$$\sigma = \frac{p - p_v}{\frac{1}{2} \rho U^2} \qquad [14]$$

where p is the pressure well away from the craft
     in practice atmospheric pressure 2116 lb./ft²
      +hydrostatic pressure $\rho g z$
   p_v is the vapour pressure of water $= 35$ lb./ft²
   U is craft or water speed.

The most critical condition is near the surface and taking $p = 2116$ lb./ft² we have:

$$U = \frac{46 \cdot 4}{\sqrt{\sigma}} \text{ ft/sec.} \qquad \text{or} \qquad \frac{27 \cdot 5}{\sqrt{\sigma}} \text{ knots}$$

Experimental and theoretical work can predict the value of σ at which cavitation occurs. This value can vary considerably depending on the thickness of the section and its angle of incidence, and increases with both. Typical values range between 0·5 and 1·0 showing that cavitation is likely to occur in the speed range 30 to 50

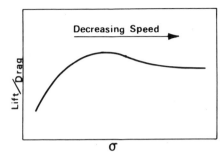

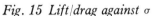

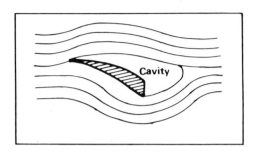

Fig. 15 Lift/drag against σ   *Fig. 16 Supercavitating foil section*

knots, and as hydrofoil yachts could achieve speeds in this range consideration must be given to avoiding this condition.

The effect of cavitation is to reduce lift and increase drag. A typical lift/drag ratio is plotted against σ at constant incidence in fig. 15.

Increasing σ means *decreasing* speed and at relatively low speeds, probably for σ>1 the lift/drag ratio is constant. If the foil is thin a slight increase in lift/drag ratio may occur as the first sign of cavitation, due to the cavitation bubbles at the nose artificially increasing the nose thickness and the lift. As the area affected by cavitation increases, however, lift falls and drag increases with increasing speed and decreasing σ, and it will clearly not be possible to work at very low values of σ.

Unfortunately there is not a great deal of information available on the cavitation performance of various sections and due to boundary layer behaviour there is not always close correlation between theoretically predicted and experimentally measured performance. As a rough guide, based on some experimental information, it is likely that a section 15 per cent thick would start to show the effects of cavitation at about 30 knots, a 10 per cent thick section at 35 knots and a 3 per cent thick section at 40 knots. These values quoted are for 'average' foil sections having pressure distributions which are peaked near the nose, see fig. 3. Cavitation will occur first at these very low pressures. In order to delay the onset of cavitation it is necessary to use sections having much flatter pressure distributions, e.g. the 7 per cent ogival or the NACA 'low drag' sections. Although these sections are superior to the average section at, or near, their design incidence, at other angles they may have quite 'peaky' pressure distributions with consequent ease of cavitation. For craft designed to work at speeds where cavitation cannot be avoided, 'super-cavitating' sections, fig. 16, are used. Under fully cavitating conditions they are more efficient than foils having average sections but their efficiency is much lower in non-cavitating conditions.

As an example in the use of the calculation methods given we may consider the hydrofoil catamaran *Icarus* (Chapter 8). The total area of main foils is 13 square feet and they are designed to carry 80 per cent of the total weight of 600 lb. For the foil chosen, a circular arc, flat bottomed section of 9 per cent thickness/chord ratio, the maximum sectional lift/drag ratio of about 35 occurred at an angle of incidence of 1° and gave a lift coefficient of 0·5.

The horizontally projected area of the foils is $13 \times$ cosine 38° square feet $= 10 \cdot 2$ square feet and 'lift-out' is observed to occur at 10 knots. Substituting these values into the equation for lift, Chapter 1, we obtain:

$$\text{Lift} = 2 \cdot 77 \times 10^2 \times 10 \cdot 2 \times 0 \cdot 5 = 1410 \text{ lb.}$$

This is about three times the required lift of 480 lb. and shows how necessary it is to allow for three-dimensional and water surface effects on the lift of the foils.

The aspect ratio A of one foil is $\dfrac{\text{(immersed length)}^2}{\text{immersed area}} = \dfrac{5^2}{6\frac{1}{2}} = 3 \cdot 85$

Hence $C_{L3} = 0 \cdot 9 \, C_{L2} \dfrac{A}{A + 2} = 0 \cdot 9 \times 0 \cdot 5 \times \dfrac{3 \cdot 85}{5 \cdot 85} = 0 \cdot 296$

For a lift of 480 lb. take-off speed U can be calculated from:

$$480 \text{ lb.} = 2 \cdot 77 \times U^2 \times 10 \cdot 2 \times 0 \cdot 296 \qquad U = \sqrt{57 \cdot 3} = 7 \cdot 6 \text{ knots}$$

Thus at 7·6 knots the boat will commence to lift-out but as it does so some of the foil will also lift out.

At the point where the boat has been lifted sufficiently for the hulls to just clear the water about one foot of the foil is also out of the water thus reducing its immersed area to approximately 8 square feet and its aspect ratio to 2·03. Hence

$C_{L3} = 0 \cdot 9 \times \dfrac{2 \cdot 03}{4 \cdot 03} \times 0 \cdot 5 = 0 \cdot 227$, and the speed for the hull clear of the water is

$$U = \sqrt{\dfrac{480}{2 \cdot 77 \times 8 \cdot 0 \times 0 \cdot 227}} = \sqrt{95 \cdot 5} = 9 \cdot 8 \text{ knots}$$

This compares very well with the measured value of 10 knots. The drag coefficient C_{D3} in this condition is

$$C_{D3} = 0 \cdot 014 + \dfrac{2 \cdot 0 \times 0 \cdot 227^2}{\pi \times 2 \cdot 03} = 0 \cdot 03$$

and the lift/drag ratio is $\dfrac{0 \cdot 227 \text{ cosine } 38°}{0 \cdot 030} = 5 \cdot 9$—quite a low figure. Note here that

the lift depends on the projected area but the drag on the *total* immersed area so that a cosine correction is necessary to obtain the true lift/drag ratio.

The forward foils have a combined horizontal projected area of 6·45 ft² and an aspect ratio of 6·1. $C_{L3} = 0 \cdot 34$ and take-off speed is

$$\sqrt{\dfrac{120}{2 \cdot 77 \times 6 \cdot 45 \times 0 \cdot 34}} = 4 \cdot 5 \text{ knots}$$

This figure is also close to that measured during towing tests, in which the bow lifted at 5 knots.

CHAPTER 4

Roll and Yaw Stability

SAILING BOATS operate at the interface of two fluids—air and water. The motion of these two fluids relative to each other at this interface develops the forces that propel the boat and affect its stability. This may seem like a hard way of saying that the wind blows the boat across the water, but flying hydrofoils are not that simple; the dynamic forces of air and water on sail and foil combine in a pattern of action and reaction that is in many respects unique. These forces, properly understood and exploited, give the flying hydrofoil the potential of being the fastest type of sailing craft—and by a substantial margin.

In Chapters 4 and 5 will be considered some fundamentals essential to the design of a stable craft. Some of the contrasts with more conventional sailboats may be startling at first. It is often helpful to take the viewpoint of a stationary boat with the two fluids moving relative to it and to each other. The concept of relative wind is a familiar one to which the concept of relative water flow should be an easy extension.

Starting with a simple conventional sailboat as illustrated in fig. 17a, the force of the relative wind will be broken down into four of the forces and moments that will be used in Chapters 4 and 5. The force developed by the sail can be viewed as a single force, R_a, acting through the centre of effort of the sail as in fig. 17a. This can then be resolved into the thrust and sideforce components, T_a and S_a, as shown in fig. 17b. Moments develop since the centre of effort of the sail is some distance above the water, which provides the reaction forces of drag and lateral resistance. The heeling moment is illustrated in fig. 17c where the sideforce is shown as acting at a height, d, above the centre of lateral resistance provided by the centreboard. This results in a heeling moment of dS_a in addition to sideforce S_a. Likewise, the pitching moment is illustrated in fig. 17d where the thrust is applied at a point d^1 above the drag force on the hull, D_h. These two forces and two moments, along with the force of gravity, are the primary stimuli to which the hydrofoil system must react properly if a stable craft is to result.

In the flying hydrofoil, the foil system replaces the hull and centreboard as the reaction mechanism. For these stability discussions, the hull or float system of the hydrofoil boat will be ignored as being a necessary appendage at taxi speeds and at rest, but not a consideration at operational speeds where the boat is foil-borne. The sideforces will be covered in this chapter, and the thrust forces in Chapter 5.

The centreboard or keel in a conventional boat, as illustrated in fig. 17c, serves primarily to develop lateral resistance. It also provides some damping of roll motion in a seaway. Unless a keel is weighted, it makes almost no contribution towards countering the sideforce moment. In a flying hydrofoil the foil system provides the lateral resistance. It also develops a significant countermoment opposing the sideforce moment, thus reducing the amount of leverage required of the crew to hold the boat level. As will be seen, it is theoretically possible to design a foil system that will heel into the wind.

Chapters 7, 8 and 9 show various successful foil systems in use. In all cases they employ dihedral in some manner as a part of the roll stabilization mechanism. The dihedral angle will appear quite high to those familiar with its use in aircraft, and rightly so, because the use of dihedral in flying hydrofoils differs significantly from its use in aircraft.

To illustrate the basic forces involved, the very simple two-foil system of fig. 18 will be used. View (a) of the figure is a section through the boat at the point of attachment of these two foils. The direction of boat motion is assumed to be perpendicular to the page. In fig. 18a it is assumed that the sideforce is absent and

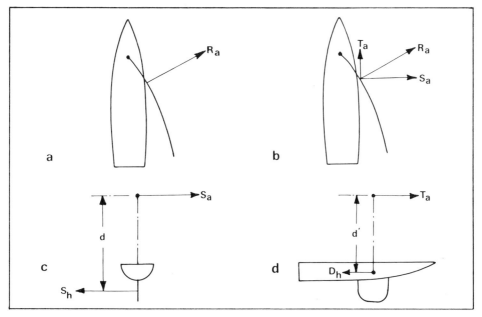

Fig. 17 (a) Force produced by sail; (b) Sailforce resolved into thrust and sideforce; (c) Heeling moment; (d) Pitching moment

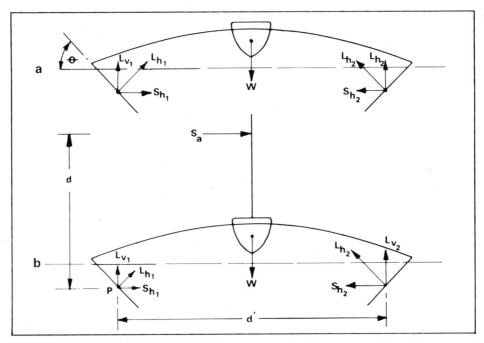

Fig. 18 (a) Basic forces on two-foil system resolved into vertical and horizontal components; (b) Effect of sideforce on two-foil system

the boat is being towed straight into the page. Under these conditions, the hydrodynamic lift forces, L_{h1} and L_{h2} are equal. They have been resolved into their horizontal and vertical components. At equilibrium conditions, the weight of the craft will be supported by the vertical forces:

$$L_{v1} + L_{v2} = W \qquad [15]$$

It is seen that the horizontal forces, being equal and opposed, cancel to give a net sideforce of zero.

$$S_{h1} + S_{h2} = 0 \qquad [16]$$

This is quite in order for a towed system with no external sideforces applied.

In fig. 18b a sideforce, S_a, has been added at a distance d above the centre of effort of the foils to simulate the sideforce applied at the height of the centre of effort of the sail. The boat will now tend to slip to the right under the influence of this sideforce, or, under the earlier mentioned concept of relative motion of the water, the water is no longer streaming perpendicularly out of the page. It is emerging at an angle to the left of the viewer equal to the yaw, or drift angle, λ, of the boat. This has the effect of increasing the angle of attack on the starboard foil and decreasing the angle of attack on the port foil. The change in foil angle of attack, $\triangle a$, varies with the yaw angle λ in the relationship:

$$\triangle a = \lambda \sin \theta \qquad [17]$$

(where θ is the angle of dihedral.) This changes their lift coefficients with the result that L_{h_2} is increased and L_{h_1} is decreased. Looking first at the horizontal components, S_{h_1} and S_{h_2}, it is seen that they no longer cancel, but have a net force to the left. This force is equivalent to the corresponding force on a centreboard, and its magnitude for equilibrium with sideforce S_a is developed in exactly the same way. Under the influence of sideforce S_a, the boat will yaw by an amount (angle) just necessary to generate differential lifts on the two foils such that the horizontal forces add to zero, i.e., sideforce S_a is exactly compensated.

$$S_a + S_{h_1} + S_{h_2} = 0 \qquad [18]$$

Turning to the vertical forces (assuming for the moment that the boat remains level) it is seen that L_{v_1} has decreased by the same amount that L_{v_2} has increased, thus the total vertical lift has not changed, and the weight of the boat is supported as before, or

$$L_{v_1} + L_{v_2} = W$$

as before.

The real contrast between the action of a centreboard and the action of hydrofoils with dihedral arises from the moments that result. The sideforce applied at height d above the centre of effort of the foils generates a clockwise heeling moment, M, of magnitude

$$M = dS_a \qquad [19]$$

A centreboard provides only lateral resistance. The two hydrofoil forces, by contrast, being spaced a distance d^I apart, form a moment with their unequal vertical components,

$$M^I = d^I \frac{L_{v_1} - L_{v_2}}{2} \qquad [20]$$

Thus the hydrofoil action is seen to generate a moment opposite to the heeling moment, while no similar advantage is obtained from a centreboard. As a result of practical design compromises, the compensating moment is less than the heeling moment, and the craft tends to heel. The deficiency can readily be made up by the crew sitting to windward.

It is interesting to note what happens if the craft is simply allowed to heel a little. This will result in an increase in the submerged area of the starboard foil and a corresponding decrease in the submerged area of the port foil. These unequal areas will cause L_{h_2} to increase and L_{h_1} to decrease just as with the differing attack angles caused by sideslip described earlier. The earlier analysis showed that the sideslip, or yaw angle, adjusts itself to result in the proper difference in lifts between the two foils for the generation of a net compensating horizontal force. It follows that if some of this necessary difference in lift is developed by differing submerged areas when heeled, the amount of sideslip required will be less. Thus,

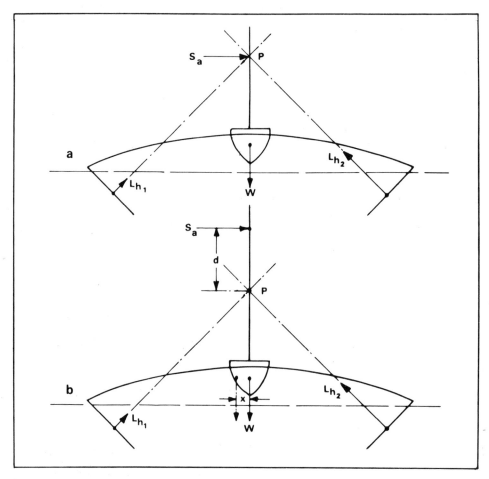

Fig. 19 (a) Exactly compensated foil stabilization system; (b) Undercompensated foil system

this hydrofoil configuration exhibits the usual characteristic of decreasing yaw angle with increasing angle of heel. In fact, it can be shown that under certain heeling conditions the slip may not only fall to zero, the craft may actually slip upwind.

The conditions for an exactly compensated hydrofoil and sail system are illustrated in fig. 19a. Theoretically such a boat will not heel under steady state conditions, and this will hold true on all points of sailing. The requirement for exact compensation is that no net roll moment shall exist when the centre of gravity of the boat and crew is on the centreline of the boat. L_{h1} and L_{h2} are unequal due to the sideslip induced by sideforce S_a as previously discussed; these forces intersect on the centreline of the boat at point P, and the sail has been designed to have its centre of effort at the height of point P. Thus all forces, including gravity (W), intersect at point P in the vertical plane centreline of the boat. Selecting point P as the point about which to take the moments, each is seen to be equal to zero.

Therefore the boat has no net roll moment with the crew weight on the centreline. It has been fully compensated through foil action alone.

However, the centre of effort of the sail seems a little low for a high-aspect-ratio high-performance sail. This then is the compromise. To obtain a high-performance sail, the centre of effort of the sail moves up as in fig. 19b. The moment about point P is no longer zero. Obviously, the beam could be widened to re-establish the conditions of fig. 19a, but this is usually undesirable from the standpoint of weight, strength, and rigidity. The dihedral could be changed, but an analysis later in this chapter will show that it is limited to a relatively narrow range in the vicinity of $40°$.

Thus, the conditions of fig. 19b are those typically encountered when all the design compromises are considered. The centre of effort of the sail will be some appreciable distance above the intersection of the hydrofoil lift vectors, and the boat will tend to heel. Taking moments about point P, only force S_a has a moment, and this is

$$M = dS_a$$

or the net clockwise roll moment of the system. To hold the boat *level*, the crew can sit to the left, shifting the centre of gravity off-centre by an amount x as indicated by the dotted W vector to again bring the moments to zero in accordance with the relationship

$$M = dS_a - xW = 0 \qquad [21]$$

If the boat were simply allowed to heel, instead of shifting the crew weight, it would reach a heeled equilibrium at the angle where the horizontal displacement of P with respect to the centre of gravity of the boat is approximately the same value of x as in the previous case. In practice the crew use their weight to keep heeling to a modest angle.

To complete the picture, the windward-heeling paradox will be examined briefly. Assume the situation of fig. 19a, except that a very low aspect ratio sail has been substituted such that the sideforce now impinges *below* point P; its moment is now counterclockwise about point P, giving a windward heel moment. Another way to visualize this is to view the craft as being supported by vectors L_{h1} and L_{h2} resolved to point P as a pivot point with the craft forming a pendulum suspended from this point. Sideforce applied above or below this point would cause the pendulum to be displaced in opposite directions. Applied at point P, no displacement would result and the condition illustrated in fig. 19a would exist.

Under conditions of induced yaw a restoring force comprising the vector sum of the horizontal components of the foil lift vectors comes into play, and within limits, yaw (or side-slip) which is a function of the angle of heel, can be reduced by allowing some heel. Factors affecting the selection of the proper angle of dihedral for controlling roll have been discussed, and yaw control by this means will now be dealt with.

The simple two-foil system of fig. 18a will be used to discuss the choice of dihedral angle. The same concepts may be extended to more elaborate systems such as full Vee foils.

It can be shown, with accuracy quite adequate for design purposes, that the yaw angle for the foil system of fig. 18a is

$$\lambda = \frac{S_a \, (a - a_0) \cos \theta}{W \sin^2 \theta} \qquad [22]$$

Note that all of the coefficients of S_a in equation 22 are boat parameters fixed by the design. Thus the yaw angle is a linear function of the sideforce, and is independent of boat speed and submerged foil area. Two assumptions used in the derivation should be noted—that the boat is level, and that the curve of coefficient of lift *vs* angle of attack is linear. This particular form of equation 22 is especially useful in analysing the yaw characteristics.

The ratio $\cos \theta / \sin^2 \theta$ in equation 22 tends to set a lower limit on the selection of a dihedral angle. This trigonometric ratio has been plotted in fig. 20 where it may be seen that the ratio, and hence the yaw, begins to increase quite rapidly for values of dihedral much below 40°. This curve suggests a practical lower limit of perhaps 30° or so. The vertical lift of a foil system with dihedral is proportional to the horizontal projection of the planform area, and is reflected in the $\cos \theta$ term in equation 22. Since foil area must be held to a reasonable value for the obvious reasons of drag, structure, draft, and others, the upper limit in selecting the angle of dihedral is related to the $\cos \theta$ factor. A cosine curve has been plotted in fig. 20 to permit direct comparison between this lift loss factor and the yaw angle factor, $\cos \theta / \sin^2 \theta$. A somewhat arbitrary upper limit for the angle of dihedral has been shown at 50°. This is the value of θ where further decrease in the $\cos \theta$ factor is assumed to be unacceptable. Thus the practical range of dihedral for this type of foil configuration narrows to about 30° to 50°. A figure of 40° is a good compromise. A flying hydrofoil with a dihedral angle in this range will have a calculated yaw angle of about $\frac{1}{2}$ to $\frac{1}{3}$ that of a typical centreboarder. This means that yaw angles under foil-borne conditions will be in the order of 2°. With such a low angle, there is very little incentive for improvement at the sacrifice of lifting efficiency.

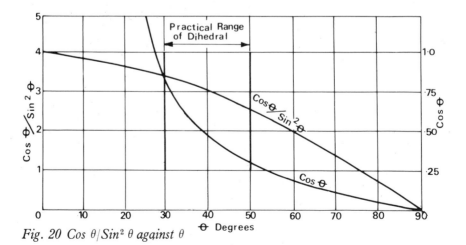

Fig. 20 *Cos θ/Sin² θ against θ*

CHAPTER 5

Vertical and Pitching Stability

VERTICAL STABILITY is indicated by a smooth and controlled rise from the flotation mode on to the foils, and then on through the speed range of the craft. Porpoising and uncontrolled dives back into the water are manifestations of vertical instability and inadequate pitching moment control.

The thrust force of the sail is applied at a distance above the centre of drag of the foil system, and therefore results in a forward pitching moment, as in any sailing boat. Any vertical stabilization scheme must at all times consider this pitching moment, and must provide for both steady state and transient conditions. Sudden puffs of wind must be absorbed without loss of control. A dive back to the surface would result in a sharp increase in drag, causing a rapid deceleration and in the extreme case a forward capsize. Some experimental hydrofoil boats have suffered from this tendency to capsize forward. The reasons will become clear as the discussion progresses.

Hydrofoil systems are generally of two types, surface piercing and fully submerged. Almost all sail-powered flying hydrofoils have taken the surface-piercing approach. It is simpler, and it has some compelling lift/drag ratio advantages when the wide range of operational speeds typical of sail power is considered. However, there are some advantages on the side of fully submerged foils, such as virtual elimination of the ventilation problem, the design option of deeper-running foils in a seaway, and less loss of lift from surface effects. Christopher Hook, and perhaps others, are developing fully submerged incidence-controlled foils for sail-powered craft. Both systems will be discussed, but primary attention will be devoted to the more widely used surface-piercing-foil approach.

The fully submerged systems will be discussed first. All of these have three basic elements—a surface sensing device, a feedback system, and a lift control mechanism. Christopher Hook pioneered the surface feeling ski, or float, with his powered hydrofin series. Feedback was through a mechanical linkage and damping mechanism that varied the angle of incidence of the control portion of the foils. This system is being adapted to sail power.

Heavy Russian powered craft have used the surface proximity effect described in Chapter 3, in which the rapidly decreasing lift from about one chordal depth to the surface provides direct degeneration of the lift. This is frequently referred to as the Alexeyev system, after Dr. Alexeyev who developed it for shallow draught vessels plying Russian rivers and canals. With this fully submerged system, the foils themselves become the surface sensing mechanism, with the feedback and lift variation functions inherent in the surface proximity effect phenomenon. This system appears to be more applicable to very heavy craft that are required to operate in relatively shallow protected waters. This approach appears impractical for flying hydrofoil sailboats. The principle of surface proximity effect has, however, been applied to the design of stabilizing foils for sailing trimarans (by Nigg, Chapter 7).

Another approach, or class of approaches, for fully submerged foils is a surface sensing system that measures the distance from the hull to the water by sonic or other instrumentation means. The signal from this sensing element then passes through a power amplifying feedback system that drives actuators connected to the control surfaces of the foil system. A number of variations of this approach are applied to powered hydrofoil boats. It does not appear that this approach has been attempted with sail power.

J. G. Baker's experimental flying hydrofoil, *Monitor*, *circa* 1955, used surface-piercing ladder foils (fig. 55). A unique feature of this boat was its automatic variable incidence control on the single rear ladder foil. In effect this boat employed the control elements of a fully submerged foil system in achieving compensation for the pitching moment of sail thrust. This system continuously measured the forces on the rigging and determined the pitching moment of the sail by means of a mechanical computer. A motion proportional to this pitching moment was linked to the rear foil assembly where it continuously varied the angle of incidence of the whole assembly. Thus a dynamic counter-moment was developed that neutralized the pitching moment and maintained the trim of the craft. A slight bias was introduced into the system in the direction of over-compensation. This bias induced a moderate climbing attitude in the presence of a thrust increase from the wind. All energy to run this regulating system was derived from the sail.

Monitor used a similar force-sensing system and mechanical linkage as a part of its roll compensation, producing a differential change in angle of attack of the port and starboard foils. This mechanism had the net effect of reducing the yaw angle required to develop the same differential attack angles as would otherwise have been developed through sideslip alone, as described in Chapter 4. The dihedral of *Monitor*'s main foil system was 40°. One might question the value of further reducing the inherently low natural yaw angle of a craft with 40° of dihedral, at the cost of the added complexity introduced.

The vertical stabilization of fixed surface-piercing foils will be described with reference to the simple system of fig. 21a. This system will be recognized as an extension of the two-foil conceptual sketch of fig. 18a, as used in Chapter 4 for the

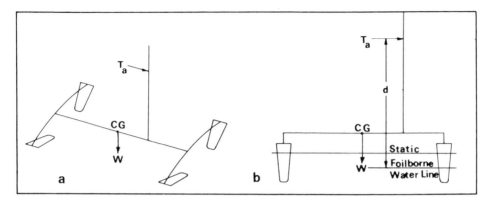

Fig. 21 (a) Four-foil system to illustrate vertical stabilization; (b) Moments produced by sail thrust

sideforce discussions. Fig. 21a depicts fore and aft sets of foils. Certain simplifying assumptions have been made: steering is ignored as is the sideforce vector of the sailforce; the thrust vector, T, of the sailforce is shown acting in the vertical centreline plane of the boat, rather than somewhat to one side as in the actual case (fig. 18b). Four single-surface foils have been shown. These could just as well have been ladder foils, Vee foils, or some combination. Likewise, a three-point rather than a four-point system could have been used, having the single foil either fore or aft—the principles involved are common to all.

A fixed foil system, such as in fig. 21a, rises higher in the water as its speed increases. Neglecting vertical accelerations, the lift at all times equals the weight. Thus the lift is really a constant, and is related to the speed of the boat by the basic equation:

$$\text{Lift} = \tfrac{1}{2}\rho C_L S U^2 \cos\theta \qquad [23]$$

Thus for the lift to remain constant as the speed increases, the product $C_L S$ must decrease. Rising from the surface reduces the submerged area, and a change in trim attitude of the boat can be used to reduce the lift coefficient, C_L, of fixed incidence foils. The lift coefficient may also decrease to a degree as the submerged area is reduced because of a lower aspect ratio and because the surface proximity effect influences the lift of a greater percentage of the foil area, see Chapter 3. If the boat can be designed with a nose-up attitude at takeoff, advantage can be taken of the high lift coefficient developed by a high foil angle of attack. Then if the design is such that this positive attitude gradually decreases as the boat rises, the values of both C_L and S will be seen to decrease as the speed increases. The lift remains constant with increasing speed as the craft rises from the water in a manner that adjusts the foil angles of attack and submerged areas to equilibrium values for each speed. The sequence is degenerative, and therefore inherently stable. Indeed, this is the underlying mechanism for height stabilization in most surface-piercing

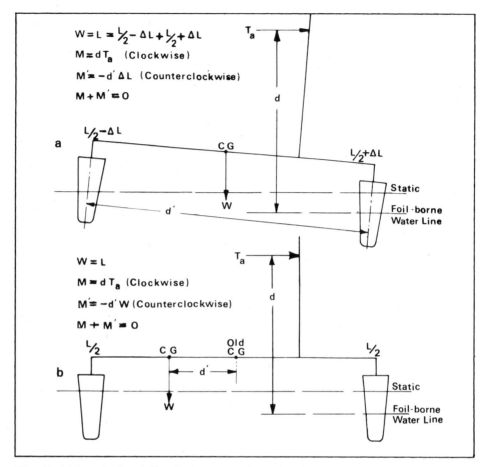

Fig. 22 (a) Vertical stability by increased front foil immersion; (b) Vertical stability by shifting centre of gravity aft

systems, but the presence of the pitching moment and the realities of transient response require some additional considerations.

In fig. 21b the four foils have been assumed to be identical and the centre of gravity is shown as being at the geometric centre of the craft. Therefore, in this simple system each foil bears the same load—until the thrust vector, T_a of the sail-force is applied. This thrust vector is applied at a distance, d, above the centre of drag resistance of the foil system resulting in a clockwise pitching moment.

$$M = dT_a \qquad [24]$$

A compensating countermoment must be developed, or the system will simply roll over forward. Fig. 22a illustrates one way the simple system might develop the required countermoment. The bow will tend to bury and the stern will tend to rise until the differential lifts shown ($\triangle L$) are developed. These $\triangle L$'s are spaced d' apart. Being of opposite sense, they form a couple with a magnitude and rotational sense of $-d^1 \triangle L$, as shown in the moment equations. The moments now add to zero, and a forward capsize has been arrested.

All is not well with such a system because its range of usefulness is limited. Note that the angle of attack of all foils has been reduced, hence the coefficient of lift has been reduced. Therefore the submerged area must increase to develop the total lift necessary to support the craft. The whole system will ride lower in the water. This might not be considered a problem with the rear foils where the load has been lightened—in fact, the rear foils may well ride higher under heavy thrusts. It is an entirely different story at the bow. Here more load $(+\triangle L)$ must be carried, *and at a reduced lift coefficient*. This compounds the need for increased front foil submerged area and results in a strong tendency to bury the nose—particularly in transient puffs of wind before the boat has had time to respond with an increase in speed, and thereby develop some additional lift at the bow. This is a far more delicate balance than in the case of a displacement or planing hull where, relatively, quite small angles of pitch develop the required countermoment very quickly. Clearly, some additional compensation measures must be taken for sailing hydrofoils.

The first of these is simply to shift the centre of gravity of the boat aft by both design and crew deployment. Fig. 22b shows a balanced condition where the weight has been shifted aft by the distance d^1 to again bring the sum of the moments to zero, as indicated. In this example the boat remains level and the lift coefficients are unchanged. In practice the thrust vector, T, is not constant, but varies with the wind. However, the crew can sit at the best location for the average thrust prevailing at the time, and lean fore and aft as required by the varying thrust. The system can be designed to minimize crew weight movement for pitch stability: the first step is to move the centre of gravity behind the balance position indicated in fig. 22b. This gives the craft a nose-up attitude, or a favourable bias for coping with a sudden increase in thrust. The second step is to operate the front and rear foil systems at different points on the lift coefficient *vs* angle of attack curve.

Fig. 23 shows a typical curve. At the speed at which the craft rides level, the operating point of the rear foils has been selected as point R, with a lift coefficient of 0·5. The operating point of the front foils has been selected as point F, with a lift coefficient of 0·9. If a sudden increase in wind depresses the bow, so that the angle of attack of each foil is reduced by $3°$, the foil operating points become F^1 and R^1. The front foil coefficient falls from 0·9 to 0·6, for a 33 per cent loss of lift. At the same time, however, the rear foil coefficient falls from 0·5 to 0·2, for a 60 per cent loss of lift. This is the crux. By operating the front foil relatively higher on the lift coefficient curve, a nose-down transient will cause a smaller *percentage* drop in lift at the front. In other words, when the bow is driven downward, the increasing front foil lift due to increasing submerged foil area suffers *less* degeneration from the falling attack angle the *higher* the initial operating point on the curve. Tracing the sequence of events will make this clear.

Assume the craft has just encountered the sudden thrust increase that has shifted

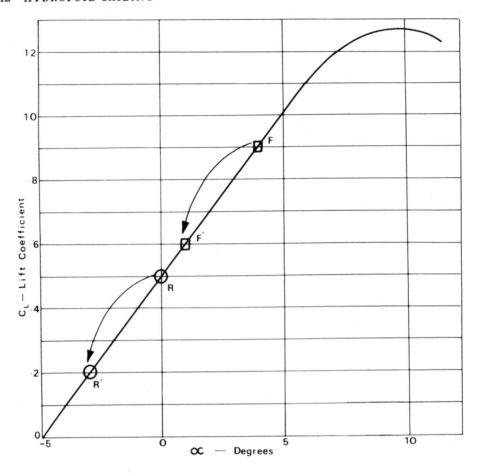

Fig. 23 Vertical stability by varying front and rear angles of incidence

the operating points to F^1 and R^1 in fig. 23. This has driven the nose down to where its submerged area has probably increased several fold so that its net lift has actually increased quite substantially. Meanwhile, the relatively larger 60 per cent loss of lift coefficient on the rear foils is causing the stern to settle rapidly. At the same time, the craft is probably accelerating under the influence of the sudden thrust increase. As the stern settles, the attack angles of *all* foils increase. The increasing velocity and the recovery of the attack angle on the front foil system combine to give the bow of the craft an additional upward thrust, or lift, which further corrects the nose-down transient and stimulates the recovery. With a rising bow, the craft is well on its way to climbing out to a new equilibrium condition at the higher speed made possible by the increased thrust.

The point of all this is that for maximum stability the front foils should be operated relatively higher on the lift coefficient curve. This is not without its penalties. For one, the lift/drag ratio of the front foil system will suffer as the operating point is moved out of the optimum region. This can be minimized from the standpoint of the whole craft by shifting the centre of gravity even further aft and designing the rear foil system to bear the bulk of the load. The rear foil system should be designed to operate in the region of best lift/drag ratios; while the front foil system, with its lesser contribution to overall drag, can be allowed to operate at high angles of attack for best stability. The drag penalty is then on the relatively lightly loaded front foil system, and the lift/drag ratio of the whole craft is degraded to a lesser extent. In practice, this concept has been carried to the point on several craft where the front foils carry only about 1/6 of the total weight. In this configuration the front foil system becomes more of a control element than a source of lift.

Increasing the attack angle of the front foils relative to the rear and decreasing the load carried by the front foils will permit a reduction in the area of the front foil system. This reduced area must be designed in such a manner that as the nose is driven down, large reserve areas are available to develop the substantial lifts required for transient recovery. In the limit case the weight of the entire craft may be borne by the front foils as they become the fulcrum for an incipient forward capsize. This reserve area is usually provided by tapered foils and various laddering approaches. The low area needed under highspeed steady state conditions is attained by the front foil running high and with a relatively narrow chord at the bottom. These narrow chords can be used at the lower extremities where load concentration exists only at the higher speeds and where their Reynolds numbers have risen to acceptable values (usually above 500,000).

Moving the centre of gravity to the rear makes available a longer moment arm for countering the larger sail thrust moments that may, at times, approach a condition of forward capsize. Systems with high loading forward are more prone to this fate. One such example was a three-point suspension system with two foils forward and one aft. The foils were similar, and with the load distributed more or less equally among them the centre of gravity was too far forward to make available enough countermoment for the thrust moment developed. The boat capsized forward—on more than one occasion.

The part played by the crew in assisting stabilization may be reviewed; in Chapter 4, a lateral shift of crew weight was the price paid for a reasonable beam width and a reasonable sail aspect ratio. In this chapter, fore and aft shift of crew weight is seen to counter some of the thrust moment of the wind. In both cases, at least some dynamic movement of the crew is implied as a counter to wind variations. However, this crew movement is less than is expected by most centreboard sailors, who tend to over-control with body movement on their first outings. The weight movement is also different—in addition to the usual lateral shift, one must add a fore and aft component. Since both are necessitated by the same windchange, actual movement of body weight is generally on about a 45° angle with the centreline of the boat. One soon gets the feel of it and learns to move 'on the bias' in full counterpoint with the wind—keeping the bow up and the lee foils riding high.

CHAPTER 6

Practical Foil Design

THIS DISCUSSION is limited to surface-piercing foils (fully immersed foils, page 18) and is concerned with the design and construction of the individual foil. Alternatives in configuration, retraction, and steering are dealt with in Chapters 7 to 9.

The desirable features for any surface-piercing foil emerge from the earlier consideration of theory, and are as follows:

(1) High aspect ratio of submerged foil at all times.
(2) Sufficient immersion depth to minimize surface-proximity losses.
(3) Use of a high performance foil section.
(4) Prevention of ventilation and cavitation.
(5) Minimum drag from struts.
(6) Provision of reserve lift for stabilization.

1. Aspect ratio

In Chapter 2 it was seen that the higher the aspect ratio, the more nearly the lift/drag ratio approaches that of the 'sectional' two-dimension ratio, which is over 100:1 for various sections. Very high aspect ratios are limited by strength of materials and comparison with glider wings is of interest; gliders have recently developed very high wing aspect ratios, with improvement of the gliding angle from 1:35 to 1:50. However the foil has special advantages and disadvantages when compared with the glider wing. The greatest advantage of the (surface-piercing) foil is that only the minimum required area remains immersed—the yacht rises higher the faster it goes—whereas the glider cannot lose excess wing area when flying at high speeds. However, this advantage for the foil creates problems in terms of strength and aspect ratio. The required area is reduced as the square of the speed; if lift out occurs at 10 knots, only a quarter the original area will be required at 20 knots, and one-ninth at 30 knots. These small areas *should* still have high aspect ratios, and it becomes clear that strength of available materials will always be a limiting factor in design. In practice foils often have an aspect ratio of between 5 and 10 to 1 when fully immersed, and taper in a manner dictated by the strength of materials and the struts (see below, 5. *Struts*).

2. Immersion depth

Surface-piercing foils are set at steep dihedral angles (unlike glider wings) for the dual purpose of keeping the immersed area well below the surface, and to produce lateral resistance, as discussed in Chapter 4. This is another area in which strength of materials will strongly influence performance at high speeds, along the lines outlined above: the foils must be tapered to small dimensions to maintain immersion at speed, especially in waves, yet be strong enough to carry the large forces involved.

3. Foil section

Most foil sailors have used 'ogival' foils, which have as their upper surface the arc of a circle with the lower surface flat. Thickness to chord ratios vary between 7 per cent and 10 per cent. These have proved satisfactory in practice, despite a sectional lift/drag ratio which does not rise above 40:1 (at $a = 2°$). They have the advantage of simplicity, of tolerably uniform pressure distribution, and of a sharp edge (see below 4. *Ventilation and cavitation*). Various experimenters have been attracted by the very high sectional lift/drag ratios of certain NACA sectional shapes. Reference should be made to the performance graphs in Abbott and von Doenhoff's *Theory of Wing Sections* (pp. 425–686). The lift/drag ratio is not plotted as such, since aircraft requirements differ from those of the foil sailor, but a straight line may be drawn, at 45°, linking the points varying by a ratio of 100. This line represents the 100:1 lift/drag ratio. All area enclosed between this line and a performance line represents foil sectional performance better than 100:1. The section with the greatest enclosed area may be chosen. For some sections this high-performance area is short and peaky (e.g. 65_3–618) and in others slight but sustained (e.g. 65–410). It is of great interest that only sections having a thickness/chord ratio of at least 8 per cent cross this 100:1 performance line—thinner sections do not make it. Care must be taken to use the curve with the Reynolds number nearest to that relevant for the foil-size and speed under consideration (Equation 8, page 23). It is also important to realize that there is no evidence that amateur-built foils have reached the very high standard of accuracy and finish essential to realize this high performance (p. 24). As a further complication there is evidence that the foil should be sharp fronted at the air-water surface (e.g. modern 'super-tankers' with a bulbous bow underwater, but sharp entry at the water-line; also the bulbous front end of a shark compared with its sharp surface-piercing dorsal fin). Since the water-line of a surface-piercing foil varies so widely there is a conflict between the two types of sectional shape; between the 'peaky' high-performance blunt-fronted section (e.g. NACA 4412) and the sharp-pointed evenly curved section (e.g. 7 per cent ogival). For all parts of a foil which never break surface there is no doubt that the first type is the better, but for the rest it is uncertain, and suitable tank tests for sailing application have not been performed. The problem is further complicated by problems of ventilation and cavitation (see below).

4. Ventilation and cavitation

Ventilation occurs when air is in contact with the upper foil surface, and the normally high negative pressure is lost, lift thus being drastically reduced. The air may travel down from the water surface or gain access as the foil passes through waves. 'Fences' consist of thin barricades which prevent air travelling down from the surface. They are certainly more important in the high-performance foil sections with very 'peaky' lift distribution, fig. 24, than in sections with more uniform curvature, fig. 25. The reason is simply that the minimum pressure of the first type may exceed the water hydrostatic pressure at quite low speeds, and lift thus be lost by ventilation. The size and shape of the fences, and even the very need for them is more easily established by practical experiment than by theoretical calculation. However the fence shape may correspond approximately to the areas of lowest

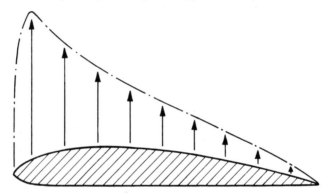

Fig. 24 NACA 4412 with 'peaky' lift distribution

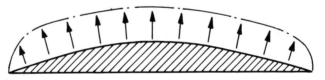

Fig. 25 Ogival section with even lift distribution

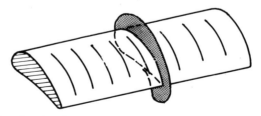

Fig. 26 Foil section showing fence

pressure (fig. 26). There is some evidence that ventilation also occurs in regions of flow separation, and the fence should extend beyond and below the rear edge (dotted line fig. 26).

5. Struts

Foils may be designed without underwater struts, but these necessarily have low aspect ratios and large dimensions to provide the required strength. Most foil sailors use a single strut, either vertical or angled, to support the foil some distance from the water surface. Fig. 27 shows a vertical strut passing up through one hull of a catamaran, as used by Grogono, on the left, and the angled, lifting strut used mainly by Nigg on the right. Further details of various other examples are in Chapters 7 to 9.

The struts carry mainly compression forces, and can usually be made strong enough with a shorter chord length than the foil has at the point of strut attachment, thus reducing drag. The position of attachment of strut to foil may well influence the design of the foil itself, since it is here that the maximum bending strains are carried by the foil when 'riding-high'. There is thus much to be said for tapering the foil only from the strut downwards, since the foil then has its maximum strength present at the point of strut attachment. The length of the tapering 'unsupported end' is then dictated by the strength of materials. If the whole boat's weight can be

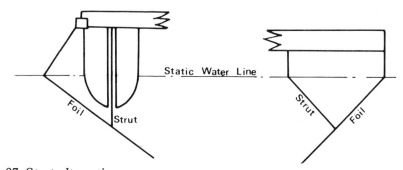

Fig. 27 Strut alternatives

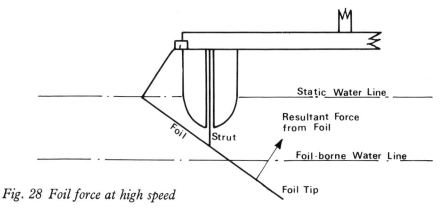

Fig. 28 Foil force at high speed

carried on the foil tips it is likely to be strong enough for sailing, but it is possible that this provides an unnecessary reserve of strength. Provided that the foils are easily retracted, so that the boat will never have to take the ground on them, it is sufficient that the load be carried at the calculated point some way from the tip (fig. 28).

6. Reserve lift

This is discussed in detail in Chapters 4 and 5. The problem of reserve lift for stability purposes is one area in which low aspect ratio pays: a low aspect ratio foil, if immersed more deeply by a sudden gust or crew movement, generates a large increase in lift because the total lifting area is increased rapidly. The same change in a high aspect ratio foil produces relatively little increase in lift—the foil must be immersed to a considerably greater extent to overcome the same transient extra force. One way of overcoming this problem is by laddering high aspect ratio foils (fig. 54), but this introduces added complexity to the design.

Each foil sailor finds his own compromise between the various factors listed above. There has been much more frequent use of wood than metal in foil construction, and a few important practical points are made here as an aid to wooden foil construction. These lessons were learned during the progression through the various sets of foils for *Icarus* (fig. 47).

Many foil sailors have made their foils out of solid planks. Oak is popular for this purpose, since softer woods tend to warp, and also to split easily at the thin foil edges. However, oak is expensive, heavy, and tough to plane, and a very satisfactory method has been developed out of laminating a semi-hard mahogany-type wood called 'Agba'. The process of laminating greatly increases the strength of the foil and also eliminates the tendency to warp. The method to be described also involves a large saving in both wood and labour-time, and is thus particularly suitable for amateur usage.

Suppose the foil is to be laminated from a $1\frac{1}{4}$ in. thick Agba plank planed smooth on both surfaces, and of similar length to that required of the foil. First, the foil cross section (maximum dimensions) should be drawn, and considered to consist of a series of laminates of $1\frac{1}{4}$ in. *width*, fig. 29. This section can be formed by cutting the laminates to the appropriate (and varying) *height* from the edge of the plank, and then turning each through a right angle in the long axis, fig. 29, before gluing-up. By this means there is a great saving of wood, and the labour is reduced to that of 'rounding-off-the-corners' and checking the final shape accurately with templates. An untapered foil is formed by this means, but the method can be further adapted for tapering foils; the individual strips may be tapered at the appropriate place, during the process of sawing-up, and the entire tapered foil formed with the minimum of effort. The laminates are glued with any water-proof marine glue, the foil planed up to fit the templates at chord-lengths an inch apart, and the sharp edges strengthened with two layers of fibreglass. This method of foil construction is fast and simple and has so far proved reliable.

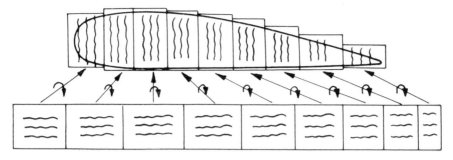

Fig. 29 Laminating technique, each laminate is turned 90°

However the process of strut attachment is more laborious. The strut itself is laminated in a similar way to the foil, to a suitable symmetrical shape (e.g. NACA 0012). The lengthy task is that of shaping the bottom end to fit exactly, at 40° (if θ is 40° and the strut vertical) onto the curved upper surface of the foil. When this is finally done the units are screwed and glued together, using wood screws passing through the foil into the end-grain of the strut to achieve strength. None of the foils made by this technique for *Icarus* have failed at this junction.

As regards the use of metal for foil construction, there is unlikely to be any better solution than the aluminium alloy extrusion used by Dave Keiper in *Williwaw*'s foils (page 84 and fig. 61). However the die for the extrusion costs several hundred pounds, and there is no possibility of tapering. This inability to taper favours the choice of a small chord section (e.g. 3 in.) for high-speed performance, with the judicious use of laddering both to enable lift-out at low speeds, and also to provide reasonable reserve stability. In summary, the process of design of the individual foil is seen to be closely linked to the materials available, and the facilities and labour-time of the builder. Further practical details of snares and pitfalls in design are discussed in Chapter 8.

CHAPTER 7

Canard Configuration

IN THE EARLY 1960's the literature on the design of hydrofoil sailboats was not extensive. A mere handful of experimenters had worked in the field prior to that time, and their work was largely unpublished. This early work usually applied lifting foils to conventional boat hulls with traditional rear steering. Vertical stabilization from the rear fell readily into the pattern, influenced, no doubt, by aircraft design. There appears to have been no attempt in that early period to explore the potentials of the canard configuration, which consists of front steering and stabilization.

During the decade of the sixties three Americans designed and built a series of sailing hydrofoils in the canard configuration. Their work was mutually independent in the early years, and their broad objectives ran in somewhat differing directions. Publication of portions of their material consolidated some of the design approaches, but only in the period after 1966. Professor W. C. Bradfield had used the hydrofoil sailboat as a central theme for a senior design course at the State University of New York at Stonybrook since 1964. Successive classes of engineering students have worked on the various design aspects, carrying their work on through extensive full-scale testing on Long Island Sound. Their work has been generally aimed at small daysailers and racers. J. R. Jacobs, a naval architect, was interested in the long-range potential of hydrofoils for large ocean-going yachts. A sailing hydrofoil entry in the Singlehanded Transatlantic Race is his present objective. D. J. Nigg, co-author of this book, has pursued sailing hydrofoils purely as a hobby for a number of years. His primary interest has been in the theoretical and engineering aspects of their design. This chapter will cover, in more or less chronological order, the work of these three as it relates to the development of the canard configuration.

Nigg's first full-scale craft was designed in 1963. Three-point suspension similar to that of the modern iceboat was used. The early experimental platform, figs. 30 and 31, consisted of three plywood floats, or pontoons, and a simple plywood beam

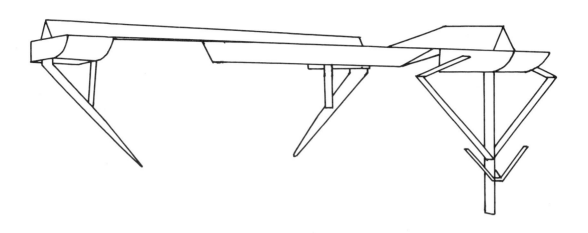

Fig. 30 Diagrammatic representation of Nigg's first craft

structure. The floats were designed with planing bottoms, as the take-off speed for foil-borne operation was above the hull speed of the short floats. The front foil system was rigidly attached to the front float and the entire assembly rotated for steering. The 85-sq.ft sail was fully battened and used a sleeve luff for leading edge efficiency. The cat rig was chosen for close-windedness and simplicity—a choice influenced by iceboat design.

All foils on this early boat used the NACA 66-S209 section. This is a difficult and time-consuming section to construct since both upper and lower surfaces are complex curves. It is not a good hydrofoil for the amateur boat builder. In 1964 the California Institute of Technology Hydrodynamics Laboratory published a detailed report on the performance of the 7 per cent ogive. Only the upper surface of an ogive is curved, and this is the arc of a circle. Nigg's later designs used this much simpler section. The original NACA 66-S209 foils were of mahogany, except for the small aluminium front foil with the $2\frac{1}{2}$-inch chord visible in fig. 30.

Fig. 31 Nigg's first craft, afloat

The original boat of figs. 30 and 31 was 17 feet long overall and had a 14-ft beam. It weighed 218 lb. all up, and had a $6\frac{1}{2}$-knot take-off speed requiring 13 knots of wind. Design calculations indicated a speed of about twice the true wind speed on its fastest point under favourable conditions. The hydrodynamic design was optimized for the 20 to 30-knot speed range.

This craft's primary mission was to study the feasibility of a canard stabilization system that had been worked out on paper, a system based on the principles set forth in Chapter 5. The weight distribution put 82 per cent of the load on the rear foils and 18 per cent on the front foil. Such a distribution was in keeping with the design philosophy that the primary function of the front foil was that of a rudder and stabilizer, not of a load carrier.

The series of events at take-off was quite unique. At speeds below $6\frac{1}{2}$ knots the craft remained essentially level. At very low speeds the support was primarily from the buoyancy of the floats. As the speed increased, planing action increased and the foils began to develop significant lift. At $6\frac{1}{2}$ knots the front foil developed enough lift to completely support its load, and the bow started to rise. The rear foils were still overloaded and the floats maintained water contact. As the bow rose, its foil attack angle increased and the lift coefficient increased accordingly. The process was regenerative and the bow rose abruptly to a new stable equilibrium position. At this point the boat had a pronounced nose-up attitude. This advanced the angle of attack of the fixed rear foils, thereby increasing their lift. The rear foil system was designed just to lift out at this new boat attitude. Thus, the boat automatically assumed the correct take-off angle of attack when it reached flying speed. No action on the part of the helmsman was required to initiate this sequence, it was self-initiating when the proper speed was attained. One of the primary design objectives was to avoid adjustments and moving parts other than those normally associated with mainsheet and tiller functions.

This first version was launched in May of 1964, and its first foil-borne run under sailpower alone occurred the same month. So far as is known, this was the first flight of a front-steering, front stabilized, sailing hydrofoil. The take-off sequence described above was quite abrupt. The bow literally burst from the surface of the water. The craft accelerated rapidly and rose to its normal running height of about two feet in a matter of two or three seconds. This initial run extended for only two hundred yards, but in this short distance feasibility of the canard approach was initially confirmed. It was stable in the vertical plane.

It is characteristic of this configuration that the bow must ride high on its front foil system. This foil forms a sort of moving pivot in the vertical plane about which the rear foils adjust their angle of attack and area of submergence, in accordance with the speed. The actual pivot point is a point in space a few feet ahead of the boat as the bow does rise and fall a modest amount with increase and decrease in speed.

At this point in the development the foil system was working as predicted. The floats were another matter. They had been designed with a favourable aspect ratio

Fig. 32 Nigg's Exocoetus, *ashore*

for planing, but unfortunately the entry angle was too abrupt and heavy bow waves developed. This resulted in a severe drag hump just prior to take-off. The floats were lengthened and the added weight was recovered by cutting lightening holes in the main stem and crossbeam. The foil system remained unchanged, only the floats and frame were modified. The bow wave problem was solved, and the boat now slipped smoothly from the buoyant mode through planing and up onto the foils. After only a few runs, the weakened main stem failed in torsion as a result of an attempted high-speed up-wind turn. The boat literally tore itself to pieces as it crashed back into the water.

The frame was completely re-designed and the structure of fig. 32 emerged. The beam was widened from 14 feet to 16 feet for improved roll stability. The foils, the floats, and the sail remained unchanged from the previous version. Only the supporting framework was new. It weighed in at 214 lb. This version seemed worthy of a name and was duly christened *Exocoetus*, Latin for flying fish.

A number of people flew *Exocoetus* during the summers of 1966 and 1967 (fig. 33). One day it flew briefly with two aboard at a gross weight of 510 lb. This represented a 'sail loading' of 6 lb. of boat per square foot of sail area, with the 85-sq.ft sail. It appears that this may be approaching a practical upper limit for these small singlehanders. It was noted that sailors who were also aircraft pilots picked up the feel of *Exocoetus* more readily. They were usually flying it quite smoothly by the end of the first long run. A lot of foil-borne sailing experience was gained with this boat, and the feasibility of the canard approach seemed well established. The results of this work were reported in the technical literature (ref. 1, page 94).

Fig. 33 Exocoetus, *foil-borne*

In the 1964–65 period Jacobs was developing and testing his canard test bed, *Experiment*. Although this work was completely independent of Nigg's *Exocoetus*, the similarity of the end results may be seen in fig. 34. Unfortunately all photographic records of this craft were destroyed in a fire. Jacobs took a somewhat different approach by providing adjustments within the design of *Experiment* that permitted direct comparative testing of several critical design parameters. Many of his results provide interesting insights, as well as confirmation of theoretical predictions.

The NACA 23012 section was selected for *Experiment*'s foils because of its good lift/drag ratio. The foils were of wood with steel reinforcing. End plates were used on the free ends of the cantilevered rear foils to minimize the formation of tip vortices (Chapter 2). Containers were spaced along the longitudinal girders to carry measured amounts of lead shot for determining the effects of hull inertia. Alternate mast steps at 6-in. intervals along the stem were provided for balance tests. Dihedral of the aft foil system was made adjustable between 30° and 40°. The original weight distribution put 30 per cent of the weight on the front foil system, but this was modified to 15 per cent early in the tests. The design take-off speed was 9 knots, and the design centre speed about 24 knots. The initial model weighed 550 lb. all up, including helmsman and 50 lb. of lead shot ballast. It was equipped with a speedometer, so good data were obtained even on the initial runs.

The first flights of the craft took place in August 1965. These were conducted in a 15-knot breeze on smooth water. As originally launched, the weight distribution and foil area deployment were designed for a relatively smooth take-off sequence starting with the front foil rising first. Interestingly, the regenerative sequence

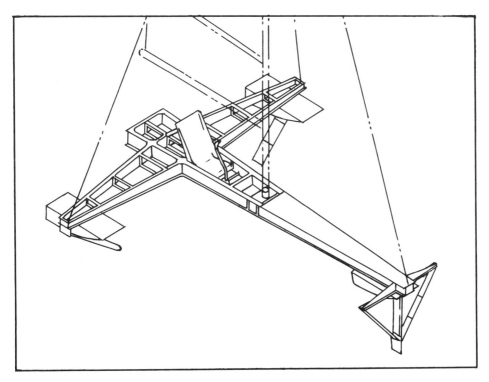

Fig. 34 Jacobs' Experiment

intentionally designed into the front system of *Exocoetus* manifested itself to a degree in *Experiment,* and although the take-off sequence occurred at about the expected speeds, its nature was not anticipated, pitching instability was encountered in the fully foil-borne mode at about 12 knots. By moving the shot ballast, the onset of this instability was moved up to 13 knots, but not cured. The problem was solved by moving the front foil as far forward as possible, reducing the front foil loading to 15 per cent, and redesigning the foil system to accommodate the new load distribution.

The second series of tests, embodying these modifications, started in rough sea conditions off Santa Monica in a 20 to 30-knot wind. The front rose at about 5 knots, as expected and, though sluggish in the heavy seas, the front foil sensing action was adequate and the pitching instability was much improved. Speeds were limited to 15 to 20 knots in the heavy conditions where heeling frequently drove the lee float into wave crests. The following day provided more favourable conditions—a relatively smooth sea and 15 to 20-knot winds. The incidence of the aft foils was increased slightly, the 50 lb. of lead shot was removed, and the mast was re-stepped to put the centre of effort as nearly as possible directly above the centre of lateral resistance of the foil system. The change in performance was remarkable. The craft rose quickly and smoothly, levelling out at 22 knots as originally intended. Above 22 knots, the expected slight nose-down attitude was observed. Riding higher

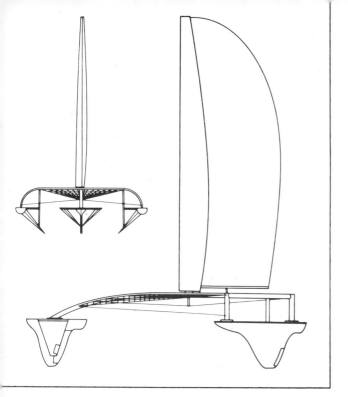

Fig. 35 Sketch of Bradfield's design (1966)   Fig. 36 Tow-testing Bradfield's 1967 version

because of the increased speed and the increased incidence of the rear foils, the problem of the lee float cutting wave crests was largely eliminated. From that point in September 1965, only fine tuning adjustments were necessary. Timed tests over a measured course were run repeatedly with each adjustment to evaluate the various possible combinations. *Experiment* was judged to have met its design objectives.

During this same period (1964–65) Professor Bradfield had been organizing his long-term student design project aimed at developing a hydrofoil racing day-sailer. Preliminary design proposals centred around equipping catamarans with foils. By 1966 the students had various original ideas for three-point suspension—including the canard system with front steering as sketched in fig. 35. Again it is interesting to note that this was evolving independently of the work of either Nigg or Jacobs; the first of the work was yet to be published by the AYRS in late 1966. During the 1966–67 academic year, Bradfield's students completed a prototype of the structural design shown in fig. 35. This prototype is shown being successfully tow-tested in fig. 36. In the following year, the float and foil systems were both modified and the craft was outfitted with a mast-aft rig supporting a roller-furling 200-sq.ft genoa. This combination was first successfully flown in the summer of 1968, and was later equipped with a forward mounted mast. This version, fig. 37, was extensively tested during the summer of 1969. Tow tests confirmed the theoretically predictable decrease of drag in the 6 to 12-knot speed range immediately subsequent to take-off. The overall boat drag/lift ratio fell from a high of 0·175 to 0·140 over this range.

Fig. 37 Bradfield's 1969 version, afloat

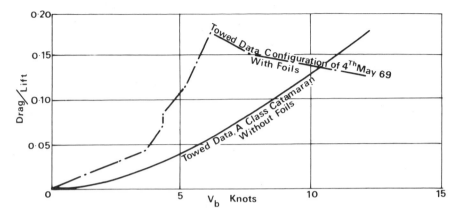

Fig. 38 Drag lift against speed (Bradfield)

Bradfield has developed an extensive performance prediction, both hull-borne and foil-borne, that his theory yields for the configuration of fig. 37. This is plotted in fig. 38.

By 1970 this continuing student project had produced a version with hulls of styroform, reinforced with plywood, and foils of aluminium and mahogany. The main foils are to be replaced in the next version by cantilevered retractable foils of foam and glass construction. The overall length is 25 feet and the beam is 16 feet. The all-up craft weight is 409 lb. to which the weight of the helmsman must be added. The front foil system carries 24 per cent of the weight in this system. A 150-sq.ft A-cat sail was used for the extensive tests run during the summer of 1970. Of considerable significance are the wave-handling characteristics observed in this 1970 testing. Performance in the short chop typical of the south shore area of Long Island was surprisingly good—in fact, the project group reports that these waves could be ignored a good part of the time. This chop builds up to about 2 feet trough to crest and has a wavelength of about 8 feet.

By late 1966 and early 1967, articles and news items began to appear in the boating press on hydrofoil sailing boats and their potentials. The AYRS, who had always been interested, and had enthusiastically reported on the slow progress through the years, stepped up its campaign to press for the full development of these craft. An increasing amount of space in their quarterly publication was to be devoted to the subject and sponsorship of development classes of these craft was being discussed. As a result of this growing interest, and under the persistent urging of Dr. Morwood of the AYRS, the design of a flying hydrofoil sailing boat specifically for the home boatbuilder and experimenter was undertaken by Nigg.

The hydrodynamic principles of *Exocoetus* were applied to this new project, but the structure was completely redesigned. The three floats were replaced by a sealed monohull, simplifying construction and providing a more rigid framework.

Fig. 39 Nigg's Flying Fish *foil-borne*

The monohull approach reduced the drag and improved the handling characteristics in the flotation mode.

To lower the take-off speed and allow full foil-borne operation in lighter winds, both the sail area and the hydrofoil area were increased. The beam width was increased by four feet to maintain the roll stability while accommodating the larger sail. Thus evolved the basic *Flying Fish* design, a rather obvious name for the successor to *Exocoetus*.

An underlying assumption was that those who might build such a boat probably already owned a small sailing boat. Sharing the sail and rigging from their 'regular' boat with the hydrofoil should result in a substantial cost saving. Under these conditions more people might be persuaded to build and experiment with hydrofoil sailing boats. Consequently, *Flying Fish* was designed around a sail area of 100 to 150 square feet, since a great many small sailing boats have mainsails in this range. The prototype model pictured in fig. 40 uses a 125-sq.ft Y-Flyer mainsail. The cost of the material for this boat, less sail and sail rigging, was under US $200. This brought the cost within a reasonable range for most small-boat sailors who might like to experiment with an exciting second boat.

Fig. 40 Flying Fish, *showing front foil at high speed*

Any monohull approach must provide some mechanism for roll stability at the dock and at very low taxi speeds where the hydrofoils are virtually ineffective. The need for tip floats at the crossbeam ends was eliminated in *Flying Fish* design by a combination of features. First the crossbeam was sealed, providing adequate dock-side stability for rigging and handling. It supports a man's weight out to the tips without submerging. The beam's elliptical cross-section provides a reasonable under-surface for water contact when manoeuvring at taxi speeds below about 2 knots. Above 2 knots, another feature usually keeps the buoyant crossbeam tips free of the water. A horizontal hydrofoil surface, just below each end of the cross-beam, can be seen in the illustrations. These surfaces, or safety foils, are out of the water when the boat is level. They are mounted with an attack angle just below their stall point to provide maximum lift. When, at taxi speeds above 2 knots, a light roll submerges one safety foil, enough lift is usually generated to prevent the crossbeam from touching the water. As the take-off speed of 5 knots is approached, the lift of the main load-bearing rear foils begins to predominate. With a little experience in shifting his weight, the helmsman can usually keep the high-drag safety foils clear of the water at these higher taxi speeds. The craft becomes fully foil-borne at 5 knots and a combination of crew positioning and foil action provides roll stability. The roll stabilization due to foil action arises from both differential submerged area and from sideslip-induced differential angle of attack on the main load-bearing rear foils (Chapter 4). The boat progresses smoothly through these various roll stabilization modes as it picks up speed, and the feel of the roll stability 'hardens up' as the boat becomes completely foil-borne.

It is in the fully foil-borne mode that a second function of the safety foils comes into play. In the midrange speeds of 10 to 20 knots, the rear foils run with a varying amount of submerged area above their V-junctions. In this speed range, a sudden strong puff of wind might tend to bury the lee foil and hook the end of the crossbeam in a wave. The safety foil develops great lift when driven into the water at these speeds and effectively prevents this situation from getting out of hand. When cruising above 20 knots the boat rides on the cantilevered tips of the rear foils, below the V-junction, and the normal lifting surfaces provide both roll stability and the safety function.

All of the hydrodynamics were optimized for the 20 to 30-knot cruising speed range. Surface piercing foil systems, as used on *Flying Fish*, can be designed with an essentially flat drag versus speed curve over a wide range. The reduction in submerged foil area as the boat gathers speed and rises from the water, coupled with the reduction in drag coefficient as the take-off angle of attack is reduced to angles having optimum lift/drag ratio, can be made to approximately compensate for the U^2 term in the drag equation. With *Flying Fish*, this compensation is effective in the region between 5 and 25 knots. Above 25 knots the drag curve begins to rise, as a practical limit in foil area reduction has been reached and the attack angle has attained its region of optimum lift/drag ratio. The calculated overall hydrodynamic lift/drag ratio for the craft as a whole is somewhat above 10 to 1 through the 5 to 25-knot region. Aerodynamic drag must be added. Thus, if there is enough wind to develop a lift-out thrust, the cruising speed can usually be attained. The increased sail efficiency at the higher relative wind velocity also helps boost the craft to cruising speed.

The hull is constructed of $\frac{1}{4}$-in. marine plywood, and the crossbeam of $\frac{1}{8}$-in. plywood. Internal pine framing carries most of the bending loads on both structures, with the torque loads carried by the skin. All lifting foils are of oak, except for the small 90° foil at the bottom of the front foil system. This foil has a $3\frac{1}{2}$-in. chord and is made of $\frac{1}{4}$-in.-thick aluminium. Safety foils are pine. All foils are 7 per cent ogives.

The prototype model of the *Flying Fish* design was launched in May of 1968. Performance lived up to expectations, and after a summer of successful trials the plans were released in the autumn of 1968.

Although the canard approach and the stability principles explored with *Exocoetus* were used in the *Flying Fish* design, there were differences that affected the handling. The larger sail and foil areas permitted operation in lighter winds. The wider beam and the configuration of the rear foils provided additional roll stability. In fact, a number of the early pictures of the trials of this boat showed it heeling slightly into the wind because the helmsman was over-anticipating and was sitting out much too far. The monohull provided the high torsional rigidity and strength that was marginal in *Exocoetus*. It also changed the trim of the craft in the flotation mode. The centre of buoyancy was made much further forward—approximately amidships—while the centre of gravity remained well aft. (In this design, only 15 per cent of the gross weight is borne by the front foil.) The craft had a definite nose-up attitude while hull-borne. In practice this simply meant that the abrupt regenerative up-thrust of the bow at take-off, so characteristic of three-point suspension canards with individual floats, was not so apparent with *Flying Fish*. It simply rose from the surface at take-off speed with a smooth adjustment in boat attitude. The front foil system was designed to be fully submerged until the bow was well clear of the water, as may be observed in the illustrations. The front foil remains fully submerged below the 5-knot take-off speed, only at take-off do the tips of the upper foil reach the surface.

There is another more fundamental reason for the low (deep) deployment of the lifting area in the front foil system. The upper (7-in. chord) foil in the front system rises completely free of the water at about 10 knots. Above this speed the $3\frac{1}{2}$-in. running foil carries the full load and the 7-in. foil becomes the safety foil for the nose-down transients (fig. 40). With its low dihedral and relatively greater area, it provides a mechanism for generating very high recovery lift for relatively small transient depressions of the bow. For example, at speeds above about 15 knots the front foil system is capable of generating a lift exceeding the total weight of the boat and crew, if the larger foil is driven to full submergence. The transient response of the *Flying Fish* is good. The 7-in. foil seldom touches the water at speeds over 20 knots as a result of thrust transients; however, it does occasionally cut a wave peak in a puff.

The design of the *Flying Fish* was optimized for a cruising range of 20 to 30 knots. On many occasions the sail on the prototype was permitted to luff because of lack of courage on the part of the helmsman—the boat would have gone faster. Tearing along at 30 knots in a small sailing boat with less than 2 square feet of contact with the world is a frightening experience. When riding on the foil tips at high speeds the smoothness of the ride begins to fade as the shallow running foils feel the waves to an ever-increasing degree. As in the case of the iceboat, and as predicted by Bradfield's theory, the fastest point of sailing appears to be close hauled to the apparent wind with the true wind slightly aft of the beam. In working upwind, the speed falls off rapidly in a manner similar to that of the iceboat. *Flying Fish* can be maintained foil-borne at reduced speeds to within about 45° of the true wind under favourable conditions.

As to the future, it appears that the canard will be commanding the attention of designers for some time. To what extent it will prevail or even survive, remains to be seen. A trend toward monohull-like geometry for canards is already evident. *Flying Fish* is a true monohull. Bradfield's students are studying high-fineness

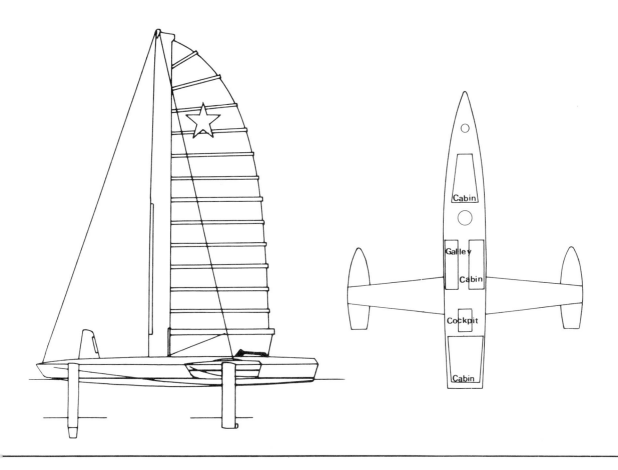

Fig. 41 Side and plan views of Jacobs' Transatlantic design

ratio main hulls with vestigial outrigger floats mounting retractable main foils. Jacobs' most recent conceptual sketch for his transatlantic singlehanded racer, fig. 41, shows a rather 'normal' main hull with small floats at the beam tips providing the low-speed roll stability. These ideas are yet to be tried afloat, and what will emerge is not evident at the present time.

CHAPTER 8

Catamaran Configuration

THE CATAMARAN configuration has much to recommend it for foil-sailing: the two hulls make the boat wide and stable; foil struts and supports are thus simplified; power to weight ratio is normally high, and catamarans are therefore accustomed to high speeds without foils—this allows a wide choice of foil size and take-off speed. The main disadvantage is that the presence of two hulls increases parasitic weight and windage once foil-borne. If the boat is purpose-built for foil sailing this disadvantage can be minimized in the design, but this is clearly not possible if the conversion of an already-built boat is contemplated.

This configuration allows considerable variation in the arrangement of the foils. In general the foils may be regarded as a 'split-tandem' arrangement (fig. 21a) but the loading fore and aft can vary widely, as can foil size and structure and the methods of retraction and steering. Three designs will be described in some detail to illustrate these alternatives. These are the projects of Howard Apollonio, of Michigan, U.S.A., and two Englishmen, James Grogono and Phillip Hansford. Each of the three was designed and completed without any knowledge of the other two.

Mention must first be made of three earlier developments. The first successful foil-cat was undoubtedly that of the American Robert R. Gilruth, head of the Mercury space project. He 'flew' a small catamaran on foils in 1939, but did not pursue the development. The next successful design was *Skid*, the double Grumann canoe of Professor Locke, of Michigan. *Skid* was 20 ft × 12 ft overall, 710 lb. wt. without crew, and set 270 sq.ft of sail to go with a foil area of 18 sq.ft. This boat became fully foil-borne, briefly, in September 1954. Two years later, in Burnham-on-Crouch, England, Ken and Terry Pearce fitted foils to their successful catamaran *Endeavour*. They just became foil-borne, but were dogged by mechanical failures. There seems to have been no advance on these technical successes during the whole of the next decade.

Howard Apollonio started his development (with the advice and support of Professor Michelson), whilst a student of the University of Michigan in 1966.

His only prior knowledge of foil-sailing was a photo and brief description of Baker's *Monitor*. The object was to produce a versatile and reliable sailing craft, and not to go for an all-out speed machine. He wished his boat to be able to sail in up to three-foot waves, and be foil-borne in a wide range of wind conditions. The outcome of these intentions turned out to be a robust, long-legged catamaran, with split-tandem surface piercing foils (fig. 42) rather similar to the successful Supramar type.

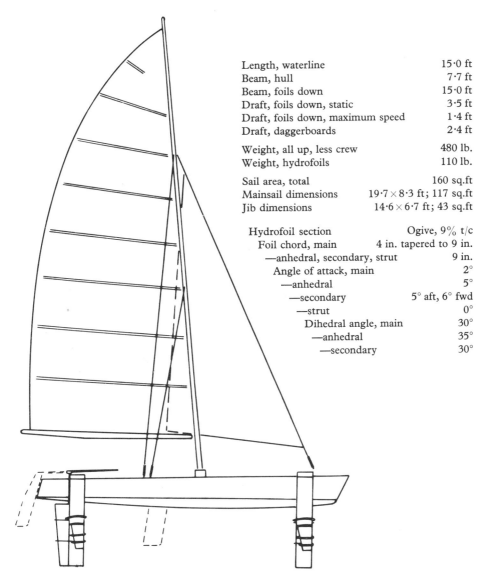

Length, waterline	15·0 ft
Beam, hull	7·7 ft
Beam, foils down	15·0 ft
Draft, foils down, static	3·5 ft
Draft, foils down, maximum speed	1·4 ft
Draft, daggerboards	2·4 ft
Weight, all up, less crew	480 lb.
Weight, hydrofoils	110 lb.
Sail area, total	160 sq.ft
Mainsail dimensions	19·7 × 8·3 ft; 117 sq.ft
Jib dimensions	14·6 × 6·7 ft; 43 sq.ft
Hydrofoil section	Ogive, 9% t/c
Foil chord, main	4 in. tapered to 9 in.
—anhedral, secondary, strut	9 in.
Angle of attack, main	2°
—anhedral	5°
—secondary	5° aft, 6° fwd
—strut	0°
Dihedral angle, main	30°
—anhedral	35°
—secondary	30°

Fig. 42 Side view sketch of Apollonio's design with dimensions

Fig. 43 Apollonio's boat, foil-borne at speed

The dimensions of boat and foils are shown in fig. 42. The hulls are extremely simple, built as square-sectioned streamlined boxes, perhaps heavier than necessary to ensure ample strength for foil attachment. They were built by one man's labour in one long week-end. Each foil unit consists of two dihedral lifting elements, supported by a vertical strut and a large anhedral element (fig. 42). All four foils have identical dimensions, a considerable saving in production time. The vertical struts are cambered inwards to provide lift to windward, and steering is effected by trailing edge flaps on the struts of the aft foils. The foils are placed to carry the all-up weight one-third forward, two-thirds aft. They are retracted by 'tipping-over' about a longitudinal pivot on the outer edge of the gunwale. In the retracted position they lie across the deck, and in the 'down' position are held rigidly by mating steel brackets, plus retaining pin, on the vertical side wall of the hull ten inches below the gunwale. The system has ample strength, but is sometimes difficult to operate in a seaway.

All lifting elements of the foils are shaped to an ogival section, with a core of Douglas fir coated with fibreglass. This technique proved frustratingly lengthy in construction, due mainly to problems in finishing-up the fibreglass skin, and also in fashioning the joints between units. These joints were found to fatigue and fail, and require heavy reinforcement with extra layers of fibreglass. With the aid of friends as available, the entire construction was carried out in 500 hours, within a nine-week period. The cost of materials was $500 (approximately £200).

The boat was first launched, and flew, in September 1967. In general terms it performs close to expectations, the best feature being rough water performance, and the worst the high wind requirement for flying. Take-off, at about six knots, requires a wind of about fifteen knots. At this moment acceleration is rapid in both forward and upward directions, boat speed rising to about fifteen knots. Higher speeds, around 30 knots, have been reached in stronger winds (fig. 43). The boat is stable in all directions, evoking the feeling of 'running on rails' with very little helm. The only hints of instability were a slight nose-down attitude, later corrected by moving the aft foils forward, and a slight tendency to a low-frequency porpoising movement. The first day's, and first season's, sailing ended when a junction between foil and strut separated at speed. Re-entry to the water was rapid, but not catastrophic. All similar junctions have since been strengthened, but continue to give trouble by delamination and cracking, as they are unable to flex to accommodate the large side forces carried on the foil units.

Further experience has brought increasing confidence in the boat's safety and capabilities; early apprehensions gave way to a powerful exhilaration at skimming almost silently above the waves, from which the craft seems divorced. Windward ability on the foils is excellent, being 10° to 20° closer winded than in displacement mode. The boat is fully manoeuvrable on the foils, but extremely sluggish when off them, a fault that would probably be corrected by rotating the whole foil units for steering instead of merely a trailing edge flap.

Sea trials were carried out off the coast of Maine, in a 20-knot wind and 3 to 5-foot waves. The boat behaved well on the foils, maintaining 15 to 20-knots speed, with much of the spray staying below and outboard of the cockpit. The foils did a great deal to absorb the shock of wave encounter, and roll and pitch stability remained excellent. There was a noticeable heave and sway motion, but the crew had a much more comfortable ride than off the foils, and at far higher speeds.

Apollonio's comments on this development, and his thoughts for the future, are as follows, with first the undesirable feature of the present version: The 'boat' portion was built unduly strong, and the added weight reduced flying time; the foils and struts are too large—an attempt to increase ease of take-off, but producing just the opposite effect—the high peak in the drag curve was confirmed by towing tests, shown in fig. 44, and was clearly visible in terms of large standing waves behind the foils prior to take-off. The use of fibreglass and epoxy resin for the foils provides adequate strength, but is excessively demanding in construction time, and he will probably use some form of aluminium alloy in future. He feels that foil sailing craft provide an almost unique opportunity to completely 'engineer' a boat design. The performance objectives must be defined at the outset, and it is frequently necessary to compromise on the purely scientific approach. He is especially interested in low wind requirement, to increase flying time, and the sail area must be ample. Stability and strength margins should be adequate, so that

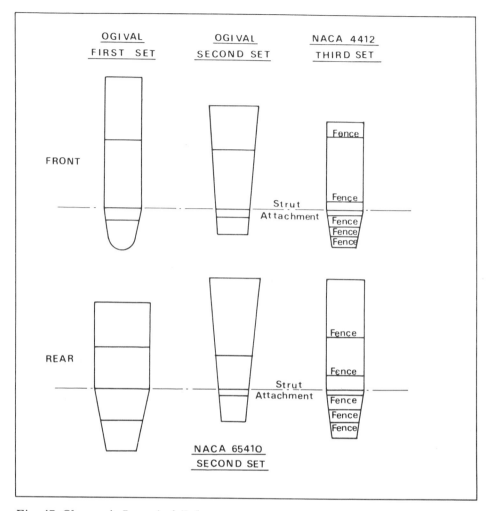

Fig. 47 Changes in Icarus's *foil shapes*

Publication of the 'Tornado' design in 1967 reawakened interest in foil-sailing, because it seemed that the task of designing an excellent foil platform had been performed fortuitously. All that was needed was to design and construct suitable foils for it.

The first year's development was shared in all respects with John James, a long standing friend and ex-Olympic oarsman. Alan Bell, of Whitstable, supplied the Tornado, which was standard except for the addition of internal hard wood blocks on the 'keel', at the points of foil attachment. These blocks were necessary to support the 'tortured-ply' construction. The first set of foils was made from laminates of Douglas fir, glued on to a half-inch Gibbon plywood base, and the dimensions of the various versions are shown in fig. 47. For the first set all foil sections were 9 per cent ogive, and all dihedral angles 45°. The foils were rigidly attached to the boat by wood screws, utilizing both the blocks referred to earlier, and also the considerable strength of the centreboard box, through which the vertical strut of the main foil passed. This vertical strut was held in position by wooden chocks above and below the centreboard box. Steering was by transom-hung rudders, which only differed from the boat's standard equipment in having extra long blades.

Stability concepts were based on those described in Chapters 4 and 5; the main foils carried 80 per cent of the all-up weight at an angle of attack of 1°, and the front foils carried 20 per cent of the load at an angle of 4°. The boat was extremely unwieldy ashore, and was at first carried into the water by volunteers, and later transported on a high-level launching trolley. On the first outing there was no wind, and towing tests behind a motor-boat showed that the boat rose easily on to the foils, and rode in a stable manner. The bow lifted clear at 5 knots, and the whole boat at 10 knots, close to calculated values (page 29).

The following day produced a 9 to 12-knot wind and she sailed well on the foils being surprisingly stable over a wide range of angles to the wind. However, she seemed to lack speed, although this was not measured accurately, and both 'in-the-water' performance and launching manoeuvres left much to be desired. The boat was foil-borne four days that year, having first sailed in September, but trials were twice cut short by failure of the attachment chocks, the second occasion causing major damage to one hull when the foil folded back at speed. This first year's foils showed that a standard production boat can readily be used for foil-sailing; failure to achieve high speed was due mainly to imperfections in foil construction and setting.

Subsequent foils (see page 48 for construction) have been modified in three ways. Firstly, all foils are retractable, so that the boat can be sailed off from a ramp with its normal rudders and centreboards, and converted for foil-sailing in deep water. Secondly the front foils have been adapted for steering by hanging them on rudder pintles, with a specially strengthened wooden block at the top, and a stainless steel bracket at the bottom. Thirdly, the area of the foil has been considerably reduced to improve the displacement performance in light airs and increase the take-off speed. The rear foils are retracted on a 'tip-over' principle, by being mounted on a longitudinal beam (fig. 48) which is strongly attached to the boat by wooden inserts into the cross-beams. The boat's weight is carried on a streamlined platform on the top of the strut.

The second set of foils, a failure, had an evenly tapering ogival front foil which was set at only 30° dihedral (a constructional error). The rear foils, also tapering throughout their length, had the complex NACA 65410 cross-sectional shape. Accurate templates of various sizes were made by photographically reducing size from a large 'master' shape drawn from the appropriate table (Abbott and von Doenoff, p. 434). The reverse curve on the lower surface was particularly awkward in construction because of difficulty in planing. The main reason for the poor performance of this set was the lack of lift, and the hulls only just cleared the water,

Fig. 48 Close-up of Icarus, *showing mechanism for 'tip-over' (photo* Yachting World)

Fig. 49 Icarus, *side view on foils (photo* Yachting World)

even in a 12 to 15-knot breeze. The only foil-borne capsize of this project occurred at this time, and was produced by slow reactions on the part of the helmsman when the boat started to 'trip' over the leeward front foil. Despite turning completely upside down, the boat was righted in about five minutes, and no damage sustained.

The third set of foils, so far the most successful, are all set to a dihedral angle of 40°, and the taper is confined to the 'unsupported-end' below the strut. This increases the area for lift-out, and provides maximum strength where it is most required. The section at all points is a modified NACA 4412. This was chosen as being simple, and versatile, and the modification consists of making the under-surface entirely flat except for the front 10 per cent. There is a substantial saving of labour in this modification, and in this particular section it involves very little departure from the 'perfect' shape. The means of retraction and steering remained unchanged, as they had proved satisfactory.

Sailing technique with these foils is soon learned by experience. Once out in deep water the conversion takes about five minutes if singlehanded. Proceed as follows: find calm water and ample sea-room, and, after coming head to wind, hang the two front foils on their pintles, and insert the retaining bolts: raise the centreboards, tip over and tie up the main foils; it is now necessary to unship the tiller from the boat's own rudders, and carry it forward to attach to the front foils. During this journey the boat has four rudders, all swinging independently, and none under control—hence the need for sea-room. Once the tiller is attached to the front foils the 'orthodox' rudders are removed and the conversion is complete. On sheeting-in, the boat gathers way in displacement mode, and is found to be reasonably manoeuvrable. She will not tack on tiller alone, and it is best to assist her through the eye of the wind by sheeting to windward on the wide main-sheet track; this levers the stern round, and is far quicker than performing a stern-board.

The lift-out on to the foils is smooth and easy, apparently easier if the boat is a little heeled. A 90° course to the true wind seems the best angle. The apparent wind comes rapidly ahead, and increases as speed builds up. For this reason the foresail must be trimmed and fixed very flat before gathering speed, since the single-handed sailor will not have strength or time to do it at speed. The foil-steering is very sensitive once foil-borne, and the boat handles well. Once riding high the helmsman's time is spent mainly in adjusting main sheet and tiller, and in fore-and-aft weight movements. The longitudinal beam provides extra leverage on the trapeze (page 2) but despite this he does not have to come in from the trapeze position once speed has built up; this is because the design is under-compensated (page 35) and is quite quickly over-canvassed in the high apparent wind. Although the boat 'flies' straight and level it does not have the reserves of stability which are designed into those of Don Nigg and Phillip Hansford. The longitudinal stability, in particular, seemed inadequate when the 'wheel-base' was shortened by moving the main foils forward. There is so far no evidence that the foil-borne boat sails faster than a well-tuned Tornado without foils, but unluckily the only comparative trials were held in 'marginal' wind, with the foils on their very first outing. Trials were again curtailed by minor breakages, and this development continues at a rather slow pace because of the shortage of time of the five part owners (Bernard, Alan, James and Andrew Grogono, and John Fowler). It remains as the only successful foil conversion of a standard production boat.

Phillip Hansford's boat provides a few similarities, and many contrasts, in comparison with *Icarus*. The hulls are of similar, 'tortured-ply', construction, and look like small Tornado hulls. However, they have no centreboard boxes, and the only rudders are foil-rudders—the boat can sail only with its foils attached.

The foil configuration is entirely original. The main load is carried on the front foils, which are located on to inserts in the front cross-beam (fig. 50a). They rotate on a transverse axis from the vertically upward 'stowed' position to the operating position down under the boat. An aluminium strut, with adjustable bottle screw, holds the foil in both positions. All of the immersed part is lift-producing, having an 11-in. chord above the strut attachment, tapering to 4 in. at the tip. Both lifting components have a dihedral angle of 40°, and there is a thickness to chord ratio of 7 per cent throughout, the upper surface being shaped to the arc of a circle, and the lower surface flat. Leading and trailing edges are not rounded. The foils are of laminated mahogany, accurately shaped to templates, and finished up to a high gloss by sanding and three coats of polyurethane.

The rear foils are transom-hung rudder foils, each having a 5-in. chord, diamond shape, with a vertical strut (fig. 50b). The pintles are mounted upside down, to take the load when foil-borne. At other times the foils are held on by heavy duty shock cord.

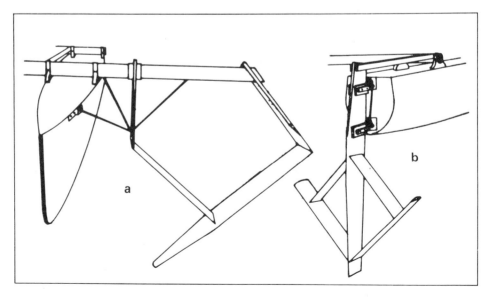

Fig. 50 (a) Hansford's boat, bow foil   (b) rear foils

Fig. 51 Hansford's boat, showing twin rudder foils

Weight has been kept to a minimum, and the boat can easily be carried, in sailing trim, by two men. The weights of the components are as follows:

2 hulls, 36 lb. each	=	72
2 front foils, 16 lb. each	=	32
2 rear foils, 5 lb. each	=	10
2 cross beams, 19 lb. and 10 lb.	=	29
Mast, boom and sail	=	27
Tiller, Trampoline, etc.	=	15
All-up weight		185 lb

The stability aspects of this boat are unusual; in the sideways axis the foils provide great stability, for although the hulls are only seven feet apart, the maximum foil beam is fourteen feet, and the design quite close to being 'fully-compensated'. It accords closely to Fig. 19b. At no time during sailing trials did the boat show the least tendency to heel, far less capsize, in marked contrast to *Icarus*. However, in the fore-and-aft axis there is a problem in setting the angle of attack of the front foils. This problem is produced by the high loading of the front foils, which carry about two-thirds of the all-up weight. It is normally desirable to set the front foils at a 2°- to 4°-angle greater than the rear foils (page 41) which in this case are set at zero, and cannot easily be altered. This difference of angle provides stability against 'pitch-pole' capsize, but normally requires light loading of the front foils, which are at a less favourable point on the lift/drag curve. Despite these

Fig. 52 *Hansford's boat, 1971, during lift-out*

Fig. 53 *Hansford's boat, 1971, showing single rudder foil*

possible theoretical objections, the front foils were set to 4°. The boat was found to lift-out easily, and sail in a fast and stable manner (fig. 51). She is highly man-oeuvrable, both in displacement sailing and on the foils, and can tack either on or off the foils, without performing a stern-board. The only problem in stability is a tendency for the bow to go down at speed, and this has been corrected by making a special seat each side to carry the helmsman's weight back almost to the transom.

During 1971 Hansford made major modifications to the rear foils. He built an inverted 'T' system, with the foil element equally cambered on upper and lower surfaces, and set at zero angle of attack. It only produced lift in relation to the attitude of the whole boat, thus allowing the stern to follow the height set by the bow foils. He used a single central foil unit with the dimensions 30 in. × 6 in. instead of double rudders. The front foils were not altered in any way.

The result of these changes was a considerable improvement in performance with the craft sailing high and stable in quite light breezes (fig. 55). The craft has retained all its manoeuvrability, but has by no means reached its full potential because of imperfections in the rig.

The descriptions of these three successful boats show wide variation in design. However, there are certain points on which the designers agree; these are the need for foil retraction and foil steering, ample power to weight ratio, and a large reserve lift in the front foil (to allow for the pitch pole force from the sail). Of less importance are the many details of foil section, size, and structure, and these are seen to vary widely.

CHAPTER 9

Aeroplane
and Asymmetric Configurations

THE TWO preceding chapters have described the configurations which seem to be most widely applicable to sailing, but a variety of other arrangements have been tried. They fall broadly into two groups: firstly the 'aeroplane' configuration, in which the main load is carried on paired foils forward, with a single steering-control foil aft, and secondly the various asymmetrical arrangements. Problems in defining and classifying foil asymmetry will be dealt with later in this chapter.

The aeroplane configuration appears at first sight to have many advantages: firstly, it retains a single steering mechanism at the back, a well-tried system in conventional craft; secondly, the resultant force derived from the sail acts directly through the leeward front foil, perhaps a stability advantage; and thirdly, the forward, load-bearing foils should easily carry the pitch-pole forces, which represent a relatively small percentage increase in loading. However, there are major problems in fore-and-aft stability; although the front foils may carry the extra pitch-pole force, the light-laden rudder foil may lose all loading, and a forward capsize ensue. It is desirable either to have controlled incidence in the rear foils, so that 'negative lift' can be produced as and when required, or to have the aft foil system sufficiently loaded so that pitch-pole forces will not exceed its load. In the following descriptions Prior's first two craft, and Baker's first, use a well-loaded foil aft to maintain stability, and Baker's second design uses incidence-controlled foils.

J. G. Baker, of Wisconsin, Illinois, built and sailed his first boat in 1950. It was a 16-ft monohull, equipped with Vee foils, and had a three-point suspension of aeroplane configuration (fig. 54). Rigged with a Snipe sail, this craft made its first foil-borne run under sail power alone in September 1950. It reached a calculated speed of just over 14 knots. Improvements in sail and rigging enabled a speed of 18 knots to be reached in June 1951, and with the addition of fins on the foil system, 'to counter the sideforce of the sail', the craft sailed at 20 knots. Speed ratios of over 1·5 times the real wind velocity were recorded at that time.

Fig. 54 Baker's first bo

Fig. 55 Baker's Monitor, *side view*
Fig. 56 Baker's Monitor, *bow view*

Fig. 57 Prior's converted Sailfish

Baker's next development, with U.S. Navy backing, was his famous *Monitor*, figs. 55 and 56. This craft was certainly ahead of its time, featuring an elaborate mechanical computer and linkage system, which measured the forces on the sail rig, and controlled the trim of the foils for both pitch and roll stabilization. *Monitor* first flew in August 1955, and her log indicates that she was paced by a chase boat at 25 knots. In October 1956 she was paced at 30·4 knots, and people close to the development of this craft report speed to true wind ratios of just over 2·0, and also that unofficial boat speed measurements close to 40 knots were obtained. There is no substantiated claim to such speeds by any other sailing craft at any time before or since.

One successful development project has involved both aeroplane and asymmetric designs. W. C. Prior, of Chagrin Falls, Ohio, first converted a 'Sailfish' for foil-sailing (fig. 57) using a light-laden rudder foil as discussed earlier in this chapter. Although becoming foil-borne in strong winds, it was prone to 'do a slow roll over frontwards, which wasn't too desirable', and a purpose-built foil platform

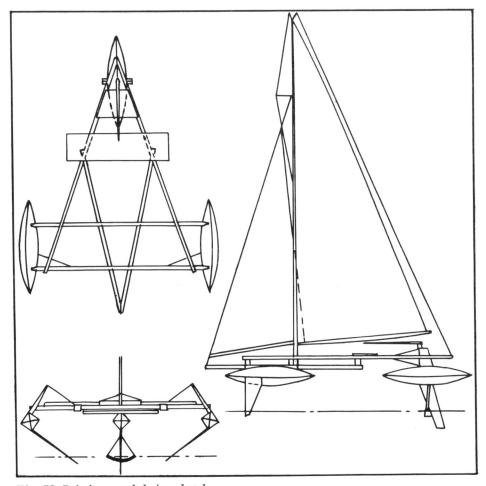

Fig. 58 Prior's second design-sketch

was devised. The framework and floats (fig. 58) are reminiscent of *Exocoetus* (page 53), except that the single steering foil is aft not forward. This craft flew well (fig. 59) but remained unmanoeuvrable and 'easy to get into trouble with'. In recent years Prior has been experimenting with an asymmetrical design, consisting of an 18-ft 'proa' hull with a sloping sail plan of 200 square feet (fig. 60). The main hull has foils at either end, and the outrigger has a single foil. In a proa the outrigger is always carried on the windward side of the main hull—the whole structure is double-ended and sails equally well in either direction. (It is of some theoretical interest that the craft has lost one plane of symmetry, about the midline, and gained another, about a transverse axis through its midpoint, when compared with a conventional craft.) 'Tacking' is achieved by altering course *away* from the wind, retrimming the sail from its opposite end, manning the alternative rudder, and proceeding in the opposite direction. This design is the most successful of Prior's various foil-boats, but he feels that it is still too impractical and accident

Fig. 59 Prior's second boat, foil-borne

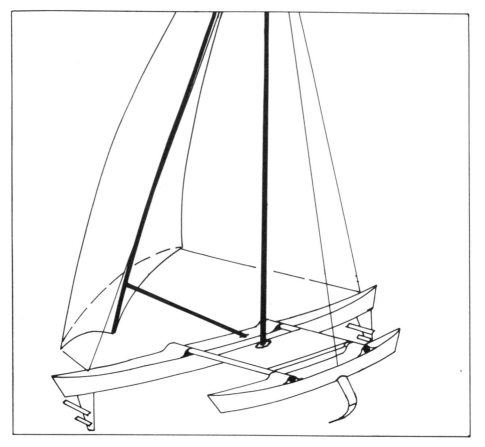

Fig. 60 Prior's foil-borne 'proa', conceptual sketch

prone. He believes that 'success in the market place' is the most important criterion. By this measure no foil sailing-boat has so far been successful. He envisages a cheap versatile day-sailer around 15 feet overall, which is purpose-built for the foils, and capable of about 25 knots.

David Keiper's *Williwaw* is the largest hydrofoil sailing-boat ever built, and the only one to cruise successfully in the open ocean. Designed during the period 1963–66, she has taken a further five years to reach her full potential—in crossing from Sausalito, California to Hawaii without difficulty.

The conventional structure of *Williwaw* is a high-sided, 31-ft trimaran, with fairly small floats and a sloop rig. The foil system defies classification along the lines of this book; the main hull has a large foil forward, and a steering foil aft, and each float has a foil on its outer side. This seemingly symmetrical arrangement is designed to be asymmetric most of the time when sailing; the laterally placed foils run less deep in the water than those on the main hull ($2\frac{1}{2}$ ft instead of 4 ft) and the windward one is designed to ride clear of the water most of the time (fig. 61).

Fig. 61 Keiper's Williwaw, *windward foil clear of the water*

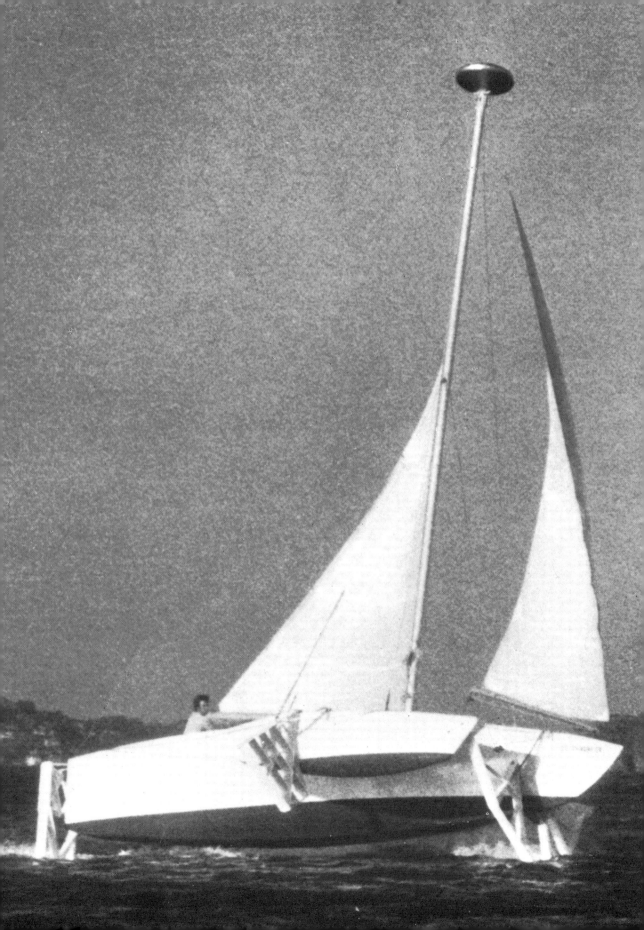

This allows the leeward foil to provide all the lateral resistance, for which it is designed, and the system proves most efficient in practice. This asymmetry is the opposite of the proa, which has its asymmetric foil to windward; Keiper's system seems to be an improvement on the proa, since the latter may have to carry 'negative lift' on its lightly laden windward foil—with its attendant dangers of breaking free between wave crests and sudden capsize.

Williwaw's foils are all made from an aluminium extrusion of about 8-in. chord and are built into ladder units by welding on to vertical struts. The small chord length ensures high aspect ratio of the submerged foil at all times, and excellent lift to drag characteristics. The arrangement of the 'rungs of the ladder', and their angle of attack and dihedral is dictated by design calculations of the forces involved. All the foil units are fully retractable, each one hinging, at deck level, away from the central point of the boat, and coming to lie on deck when fully retracted.

Williwaw first became foil-borne in April 1968, and has since sailed about 4,000 miles at sea (fig. 62). She begins to fly in winds of 10 knots, and is capable of around 20 knots in stronger winds. Keiper has encountered no major problems at sea, and often uses the foils when the boat is not fully foil-borne, because of their excellent stabilizing effect. *Williwaw* has flown, in estuary waters, with up to nine people on board.

One further exponent of asymmetric foil design, especially in models, is B. Smith, whose series of designs and experimental models is described in ' *The Forty Knot Sailboat*' (ref. page 94). His principle is that a single streamlined shape, an aerohydrofoil, can be the basis of a theoretically perfect sailing machine. His models have worked well, and a full-size version has flown briefly, but not so far at great speed.

The last three chapters indicate the range of successful designs, the 'foil platform' varying from a sailing surf-board to a cruising multihull, and the foils themselves from simple shaped planks to elaborate incidence-controlled metal lattices. What general conclusions may be drawn from comparing and contrasting them?

Perhaps the most important conclusion concerns design objectives. One objective is common to all the designs—that is to use hydrofoils to lift a sailing craft clear of the water—and all have been successful in achieving this. Most other objectives vary widely, and each design represents a particular compromise between opposite sets of factors that are broadly in conflict. On the one hand, for sheer speed, the design is likely to be expensive, impractical, and frail. On the other hand, most owners prefer their craft to be cheap, practical, and strong. The following features would be emphasized if speed alone is allowed to dominate the design:

1. High power to weight ratio. This is one of the main features determining ease of take-off and ultimate speed. The whole structure should be as light as possible, without excessive safety margins, and the sailplan ample in area.

2. Fixed foils. These may cause difficulties in launching, going aground, and weed-clearing, but they allow greater strength, and more exact setting of angles of attack and alignment.

Fig. 62 Williwaw, *at sea*

3. Aerodynamic sailplan. Appendix 2 makes it clear that a sophisticated sailplan, with a low drag angle, is vital to very high speed, and this implies an unwieldy and complicated wingsail, probably of the type popular in 'C' Class catamarans.

4. Foil factors. Chapters 4, 5 and 6 indicate the important features; the foils will be of metal, with high aspect ratio and slender tapering tips, prone to damage and perhaps dangerous to by-standers. The 'foil-platform' will be very wide, to bring the design close to full compensation (fig. 19a); this will be necessary in the high apparent winds that are inevitable.

All of these factors detract from the boat as a 'practical day sailer'; however, the designers in this volume are ardent small-boat sailors, and each therefore makes his own compromises to allow the boat to become a practical proposition. In terms of commercial outlet the departure from theoretical perfection must be even greater, since a buyer is less likely to put up with inconvenience than the designer/experimenter. There is an argument here in favour of sponsored speed records (with substantial prizes) which would encourage the more extreme designs. There is also a possible outlet for extreme designs in 'C' Class catamarans, as foils are specifically permitted in the rules of the Little America's Cup. However, these craft have become very complicated, even without foils, and many practical problems, such as retracting the foils at speed, need solving before progress can be made.

APPENDIX I

United States Patents relating to Hydrofoil Sailing Craft

1. 1,356,300 M. McIntyre (1920) 'Sailing craft'.
   Low aspect ratio foil stabilizers, similar in principle to those of Gerald Holtom, described in 1971 in AYRS No. 74.
2. 2,703,063 R. R. Gilruth (1955) 'Hydrofoil craft'.
   Fully submerged high aspect ratio foils, spanning between the hulls of a small 'flying' foil-cat, with a control mechanism.
3. 2,804,038 H. M. Barkla (1957) 'Sailing vessels'.
   Submerged floats, with foils attached, connected by struts to an inclined aerofoil system, with an elaborate control system.
4. 2,856,879 J. G. Baker (1958) 'Hydrofoil system for boats'.
   Comprehensive patents of *Monitor* (page 81).
5. 2,858,788 J. Lyman (1958) 'Watercraft'.
   A lifting and stabilizing device consisting of a single vertical fin, with foils attached. It has trailing edge flaps, set well apart, which act in opposite directions to produce a couple for stabilization against wind forces.
6. 3,077,850 W. C. Beuby (1963) 'Sailboat of the Catamaran type'.
   A system of easily detachable foils for a 'flying' catamaran, with 'aeroplane fuselage' hulls, inside which sit the crew.
7. 3,179,078 J. R. Popkin (1965) 'Dual hydrofoil mechanism for sailboats'.
   Retractable stabilizing foils automatically controlled by wind forces.
8. 3,295,487 B. Smith (1967) 'Hydrofoil sailboat'.
   Asymmetric hydrofoil craft (page 87).
9. 3,373,710 A. Steinberg (1968) 'Hydrofoil boat'.
   Stabilization of a lifting hydrofoil system by ailerons controlled by tension in the mast shrouds. The windward foil is designed to have negative lift.
10. 3,459,146 W. Prior (1969) 'Hydrofoil watercraft'.
    A system of balanced, self-correcting foils in ladder assembly, each foil being inverted 'U' shape.
11. 3,561,388 D. Keiper (1971) 'Hydrofoil sailing craft'.
    Comprehensive patents of *Williwaw* (page 84).

APPENDIX II
Thrust factor at high speeds

Few ordinary sailing boats reach speeds comparable to the speed of the wind.
Modern catamarans are an exception, with reports ranging as high as 1·6 times the
true wind on their best point of sailing. Iceboats normally exceed the speed of the
wind and ratios as high as 4 to 1 are not uncommon. Flying hydrofoil sailing boats,
with their potential of over twice the speed of the wind, fall in between. The 'thrust
factor' concept is important to any sail-powered craft capable of exceeding the
speed of the wind. This analysis will show quantitatively the increasing importance
of aerodynamic cleanness and low aerodynamic drag angle as the speed ratios
climb on these high-performance craft. The analysis will show the magnitude of
thrust enhancement available at these higher speed ratios as lower aerodynamic
drag angles are achieved through advanced sail design. The potential is truly
remarkable, and certainly justifies the growing interest in wingsails and rigid
airfoils with their superior control of aerodynamic drag angle.

The resultant sailforce developed by the passage of air over the surface of the
sail is proportional to the square of the velocity of that air. However, as illustrated
in fig. 63 this force is at an angle to the heading, and only the forward component
is useful in driving the boat. As the speed of the boat increases, under conditions
where the apparent wind is forward of the beam, the velocity of the apparent wind
increases and its direction moves forward. The resultant sailforces are several times
greater than in normal sailing boats in the same real wind, but these sailforces are
developed at an ever deteriorating angle with respect to the desired forward thrust
component. Which prevails, and over what ranges and under what conditions?
It turns out that the apparent wind velocity factor is very real, and properly exploited can give a boost to these craft at their higher speed ratios. An understanding
of this factor goes a long way toward explaining some of the legends of the ice-
boaters. It is often heard among enthusiasts that an iceboat 'makes its own wind'.
It might seem absurd that an increase in headwind can increase the power of the
sail. However, this is what happens, the key being the velocity squared term in the
sailforce equation. The following example will make this clear.

Fig. 63 shows a boat moving on a course 90° from the real wind. This course is

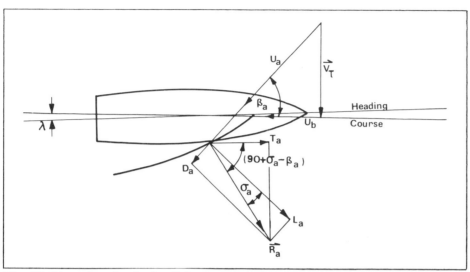

Fig. 63 Plan view sketch of sail forces

not necessarily the fastest but it is an easy one for purposes of illustration. Iceboats and hydrofoils usually go their fastest somewhat farther off the real wind, but the 90° course will serve to illustrate the principles involved. The heading of the boat is shown by a small yaw angle—virtually zero for an iceboat and 2° or so for a well-designed hydrofoil. All angles are related to true course and real wind, therefore the yaw angle will not show in the equation. The resultant sailforce, R_a is shown resolved into the aerodynamic crosswind and drag components, L_a and D_a, to delineate the all-important aerodynamic drag angle, σ_a, of the sail. The apparent wind, U_a, is shown at an angle β_a from the course. This angle will be the independent variable as the value of the thrust vector, T_a, is examined under differing conditions.

Looking at the relationships of these forces, the value of R_a is seen to be:

$$R_a = \left[\frac{\rho_a}{2} S_s C_{Ra} \right] U_a^2 \qquad [25]$$

where the terms in the brackets are constant. The coefficient C_{Ra} is composed of the more familiar aerodynamic crosswind and drag coefficients in the relationship

$$C_{Ra} = (C_{La}^2 + C_{Da}^2)^{\frac{1}{2}}$$

Thus the resultant sailforce R_a is a function of the apparent wind only. From the geometry of fig. 63 it is seen that

$$T_a = R_a \cos (90 + \sigma_a - \beta_a) \qquad [26]$$

Substituting for R_a in Equation 26

$$T_a = \left[\frac{\rho_a}{2} S_s C_{Ra} \right] U_a^2 \cos (90 + \sigma_a - \beta_a) \qquad [27]$$

Note that in terms of the real wind, U_T, which is constant, that

$$U_a = \frac{U_T}{\sin \beta_a}$$

substituting for U_a in Equation 27

$$T_a = \left[\frac{\rho_a}{2} S_s C_{Ra} \right] \frac{U_T^2}{\sin^2 \beta_a} \cos (90 + \sigma_a - \beta_a) \qquad [28]$$

Grouping U_T^2 with the other constants in the brackets

$$T_a = \left[\frac{\rho_a}{2} S_s C_{Ra} U_T^2 \right] \frac{\cos (90 + \sigma_a - \beta_a)}{\sin^2 \beta_a} \qquad [29]$$

Equation 29 is the basic equation for thrust of the sail. The values of C_{Ra} and σ_a are functions of the design of the sail, its attack angle and the degree of camber, or flatness, in operation. It is assumed for purposes of the example that these factors remain constant for a given configuration as β_a is varied over the potential operating range.

To determine if the increasing apparent wind velocity (with decreasing angle β_a) really does result in thrust enhancement in the above example, Equation 29 will be examined for conditions of maximum thrust. Taking the partial derivative with respect to β_a and equating to zero yields

$$2 = \tan \beta_a \tan (90 + \sigma_a - \beta_a) \qquad [30]$$

Equation 30 is the relationship for maximum thrust.

To better understand the significance of Equation 30, assume a value of 15° as an attainable aerodynamic drag angle for a very good soft sail. Substituting this value for σ_a in Equation 30 and evaluating for β_a it is found that the value of β_a for maximum thrust is 33°. Noting from fig. 63 that the speed ratio is cot β_a, the speed ratio at β_a 33° comes out to be 1·54. Thus, in the example examined, the thrust developed by the sail reaches a maximum at a boat speed of 1·54 times the true wind speed. Therefore, the velocity squared term in the sailforce equation does prevail, and there can indeed be a net thrust enhancement under proper conditions at these higher speed ratios. To this extent, the iceboater is correct, and his craft does 'make its own wind'.

To appreciate more fully the implications of this relationship, fig. 64 has been constructed. It is a series of plots of the variable portion of the thrust, Equation 29, for various values of σ_a. This variable portion of Equation 29 is termed the 'thrust factor' of the system, a dimensionless figure that can be used for comparison purposes. Note that for the example of $\sigma_a = 15°$ the maximum is at 33°, as calculated earlier. Fifteen degrees was used in the example as an achievable drag angle for soft sails. A value of 10° probably is not—a wingsail or rigid airfoil structure being necessary. The important thing to note is the great thrust factor improvement

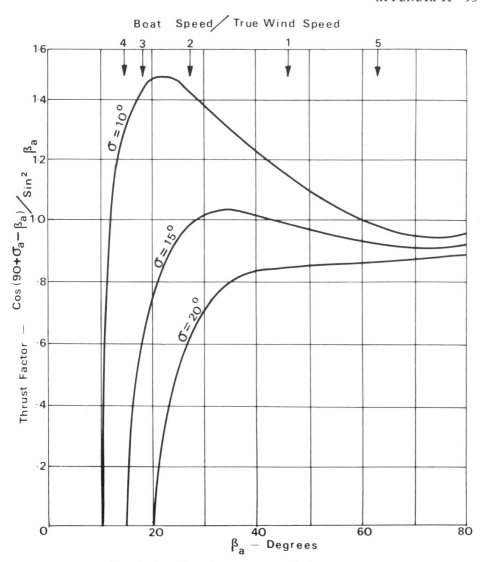

Fig. 64 'Thrust factor' plotted against apparent wind

available at speed ratios above about one, if the lower aerodynamic drag angles can be achieved. The very flat sails on iceboats operating at high speed ratios strive for these potentially higher thrust factors. It should be noted that the curves of fig. 64 cannot be directly compared to each other for absolute thrust generated. The different values of σ_a will have different values of C_{Ra} associated with them, and therefore the magnitude of the curves cannot be compared directly. The point of valid comparison among the curves is the relative ability of the different sails to maintain their thrust at decreasing values of β_a, and the speed ratio at which each reaches its maximum thrust. The thrust factor concept provides these two insights only—nothing more.

SELECTED BIBLIOGRAPHY

1. *The Elements of Aerofoil and Airscrew Theory*, H. Glauert, Cambridge University Press.
2. *Shape and Flow, the Fluid Dynamics of Drag*, A. H. Shapiro, Science Study series no. 20, Heinemann, London.
3. *Boundary Layer Theory*, H. Schlicting, McGraw Hill.
4. *Fluid Dynamic Drag*, S. F. Hoerner, 148 Busteed Drive, Midland Park, New Jersey, 07432, U.S.A.
5. *Theory of Wing Sections*, I. H. Abbott and A. E. von Doenhoff, Dover Publications Inc.
6. *Hydrofoils*, C. Hook and A. C. Kermode, Pitmans, London.
7. *Aeromarine Origins*, H. F. King, Putnam, London.
8. *Sailing Theory and Practice*, C. A. Marchaj, Adlard Coles Limited, 3 Upper James Street, London W1R 4BP.
9. *The Forty Knot Sailboat*, B. Smith, Grosset and Dunlap Inc., New York.
10. *Sailing Hydrofoils*, Amateur Yacht Research Society No. 74, J. Morwood, Woodacres, Hythe, Kent, England.

REFERENCES

1. 'A Sailing Hydrofoil Development', D. J. Nigg, *Marine Technology*, The Society of Naval Architects and Marine Engineers, 74 Trinity Place, New York, New York 10006, April 1968.
2. 'Predicted and Measured Performance of a Day-sailing Catamaran', W. S. Bradfield, *Marine Technology*, January 1970. (Address as above.)
3. 'Stabilizing Foils for Cruising Trimarans', D. J. Nigg, Issue 5, August 1970, *Trimaraner*, Box 12828, Kansas City, Missouri 64124, U.S.A. pp. 24–26 and 38.

GLOSSARY OF SYMBOLS

A	Aspect ratio	p_o	Stagnation pressure
C_L	Lift coefficient	p_v	Vapour pressure of water
C_{L2}	Sectional lift coefficient of a foil	R_a	Resultant aerodynamic force
		R_e	Reynolds number
C_{L3}	Lift coefficient of a complete foil	S	Area
		S_s	Sail area
C_{La}	Crosswind lift coefficient	S_a	Sail aerodynamic side force
C_D	Drag coefficient	S_h	Foil hydrodynamic side force
C_{Di}	Induced drag coefficient		
C_{Da}	Crosswind drag coefficient	T_a	Sail thrust
C_{Ra}	Resultant crosswind force coefficient	U	Velocity of craft or main fluid speed
D	Drag	U_a	Apparent wind velocity
D_a	Sail drag force	U_b	Component of apparent wind along boat's course
D_h	Hull drag force		
d, d^l	Distances	U_T	True wind velocity
F_n	Froude number	u	Velocity at a general point of the fluid
g	Acceleration due to gravity		
		W	Weight of craft
K	A constant	x	Distance
l	A length	y	Direction perpendicular to foil or hull surface
L	Lift		
L_a	Sail crosswind force	z	Vertical direction
L_h	Total hydrodynamic lift	α	Foil incidence, relative to chord line
L_v	Vertical hydrodynamic lift		
M, M^l	Moments	α_o	Zero lift incidence
P	Undisturbed pressure	β_a	Angle between apparent wind and boat's course
p	Pressure at a given point		

γ	Craft angle of attack	σ_a	Aerodynamic drag angle of sail
$\triangle$	Boundary layer thickness		
θ	Dihedral angle	ρ	Fluid density
λ	Yaw angle	ρ_a	Density of air
σ	Cavitation number	μ	Fluid viscosity